MUSIC FROM TAIZÉ

Responses · Litanies · Acclamations · Canons

Jacques Berthier

INSTRUMENTAL EDITION

COLLINS

Also available in this series:

Vocal edition	00 599720 8
People's edition	00 599952 9
Volume II	
Vocal edition	00 599863 8
Instrumental edition	00 599883 2
People's edition	00 599884 0
Joy on Earth	00 599927 8

HarperCollins*Religious*
a division of HarperCollins*Publishers*
77-85 Fulham Palace Road, London W6 8JB

Collins Dove
PO Private Bag 200, Burwood, Victoria 3125

Collins Liturgical New Zealand
PO Box 1, Auckland

ISBN 00 599721 6 Instrumental edition

First published, this edition, 1982
Fifth printing 1991

Printed in Great Britain
by Bell and Bain Ltd., Glasgow

Bound by Hunter & Foulis, Edinburgh

FOREWORD

The following introduction relates specifically to this volume of instrumental accompaniments and solos. In addition, it is vitally important that the foreword to the vocal edition be read in order to develop a complete understanding of the nature, style and performance techniques of this Music from Taizé.

THE USE OF INSTRUMENTS

Instruments play a important role in maintaining the steady pitch and tempo of the singing. It has already been mentioned in the Vocal Edition that a *guitar* is useful, especially for small groups, whereas for parish churches the *organ* fulfills this function well.

Without losing sight of the main purpose of this music, which is to bring about a complete participation of the assembly, *more evolved versions* may be prepared as well, provided that the musical means are present and the liturgical circumstances allow. Such fuller versions can lend expression to the successive stages of an interior meditation or the jubilation of a joyful celebration. The way is open, then, for exploring all the possibilities of alternating and combining various melodic instruments, such as flute, oboe, trumpet, cello, etc. This springs neither from aesthetic considerations, nor from a desire to make music for music's sake. It is rather a way of saying what words cannot say, and of expressing a spiritual animation that swells from the depths of the human heart.

Without a spirit of faith and prayer, this music will lose its fullest meaning. And conversely, if there is inadequate attention given to quality or 'dignity' in the musical performance itself, no spiritual message will be communicated. While the instrumental parts were not written with virtuosi in mind, careful intonation and musicianship are no less indispensable, even in the simplest passages.

The *conductor,* although he or she need not be professional, must none the less be clearly competent and have a good technique to insure the proper performance of these pieces.

Finally, aside from using these instrumental parts in conjunction with the vocal music for which they are designed, they may be arranged to form independent *instrumental pieces* in the same spirit and style as their sung counterparts.

OSTINATO RESPONSES AND CHORALES

The instrumental countermelodies should be treated in the same way as the soloists' verses, with one following another. They can be made to alternate with the verses that the vocal soloists sing. In its own way, each instrument brings fresh expression to the prayer as a whole.

The characteristics of the instrument will determine in some ways the dynamic level of the singing. A flute calls for a *piano* expression, while brass may suppose *forte* singing, etc. With each repetition of the theme, the instrument(s) will thus contribute to the constantly varying texture of the piece.

LITANIES AND OTHER TEXTS WITH REFRAINS

Refrains of the "Kyrie eleison" type, that is, refrains to texts in litany form improvised by soloists, and *acclamations* (section III in the Vocal Edition) do not have a particular instrumental accompaniment. To ensure that the pitch stays secure, it is a good idea either to double the melody line with an instrument such as an oboe, flute or trumpet, or to have the organ play all four parts. In this case, refer to the Vocal Edition.

All the *litanies,* however, whose verses are fully written out for the cantors, have an organ accompaniment for both verses and refrains as well as several countermelodies that may be played by solo instruments. These litanies may also be changed into repetitive pieces of meditation or praise, after the fashion of the pieces in the first section. In this case, the sung verses are dropped and instrumental verses substituted, or the sung and instrumental verses may be used alternately without the regularity of form that characterizes a litany.

SPECIAL CASES

Adoramus te Domine II

Special trumpet fanfares [2] are provided for the *Gloria* when this refrain is used in place of the *Adoramus.*

Maranatha! Alleluia! I

We recall God's action in times past, through the history of his people heading towards the Promised Land. Today we celebrate new life brought through the Resurrection. The music of these paschal acclamations corresponds to this double theme in structure: two cantors and two different refrains for each verse.

The style is straightforward, with strong contrasts in timbre, intensity and rhythm created through the use of very simple elements. Both simplified and full versions are possible.

The simplified version uses these basic elements:

Instrumental Accompaniement—A sustained chord in two or three octaves ending with a movement of fifths on the Alleluia.

Choir—Soft humming under the verses with energetic refrains.

Cantors—Free and spirited, with the ends of the two phrases sung rhythmically, however, so as to provide the tempo for the refrains to follow.

Percussion—An instrument with a long ring (cymbal or gong) for the refrains and two other rhythmic instruments designed to stress the contrast between the different character of each refrain. These latter instruments also function to introduce the choir's refrains by means of two simple motifs superimposed on the cantor's last note (at the dotted vertical line.)

Brass—With the assembly (each refrain, second time only).

For the full version (p. 43-45):

Instrumental Accompaniment—An appoggiatura precedes the sustained chord. During the repeat of "Maranatha" (brass and people) some instruments can drop out of the sustained fifth and improvise in the D dorian mode, simultaneously in different ways, like an orchestra tuning, e.g., rapid scales, arpeggios, etc.

Percussion—It is of utmost importance that the rhythm, accents and off-beats be sharp and clear. The gong (p. 42) is added.

Introduction—Preceding the normal development of the piece, the rhythm and forward movement are established with a rapid crescendo.

Memento nostri Domine

With minimal resources this piece expresses the intense meditation of a believer contemplating Jesus on the cross. The solo flute, in an atonal idiom, sets the mood for each of the verses it introduces. The quality of performance is thus most important.

The verses should be sung freely and simply. Improvisation is permissible provided that the text and the spirit of prayer is respected. Since there is no accompaniment, it is important that the cantor remain on pitch.

If the cantor sings each refrain accurately, the people should have no problem repeating it, even though the melody and rhythm changes from one verse to another.

Each unit is made up of flute solo, verse, response and silence. The entire prayer has eight such units any of which can be omitted or used separately.

Veni Creator Spiritus

In every version of this piece, even the most simple one, it is important to keep a steady tempo throughout. It is a kind of incantation in which development takes place by varying the dynamic levels, from *piano* to *forte* and back to *piano*, very gradually in the course of the piece. This progression will be helped by the choice of instrumental passages at particular moments, for example, using the brass in the middle of the piece for the *forte*, and the flute at the end for the conducting *piano*.

CANONS

Instruments may be used even in the simple versions of the canons. The melody of the repeated theme is sung in unison or in two voices. Melodic instruments may be used for solos played above the canon, as in the previous pieces. If the organist has the necessary ability, he or she may improvise over the theme and its harmonic pattern.

In addition, of course, more developed polyphonic versions may be devised. Experienced musicians will have no difficulty in combining the different elements that constitute each piece. Clearly, these combinations are always worked out in the framework of the basic harmonic pattern: the "units" that may be superimposed are marked off by double bar-lines and indicated by a letter Ⓐ Ⓑ etc., for the canonic themes, or by a number ① ② etc., for the instrumental sequences.

The one who is in charge of the singing and its execution participates in a real way in the creation of the piece, since each one may be presented in a variety of ways. But where more complex versions are desired, it is necessary that careful planning of the structure be undertaken, namely, that such things as entries and "tacets" of various parts, changes in the 'thickness' of the sound (by adding extra voices or instruments), in the dynamic level (by *crescendo* or *diminuendo*), and the way of bringing the piece to a close need to be well arranged in advance.

It is up to each user of this music to find the best ways of arranging the material for his or her own circumstances and resources. What follows are some practical guidelines, based on the experience at Taizé, of how a canon such as the *Magnificat* might be prepared for use. A grid will be drawn up to indicate visually how the piece will unfold, and a conductor's diagram will show the succession of entries.

Brother Robert

First example: ***Magnificat* in four-voice canon, without instruments**

A gradual polyphonic *crescendo* is created with the successive entries of different voices, spaced at unequal distances to avoid too rapid and too mechanical a combination of the four parts. First, the letters of the harmonic units of the canon are arranged in a horizontal line from left to right. The other entries are given on three additional lines so that the four lines taken together correspond vertically with what is happening at a given point in the music. What results is a kind of score. If the letter "A" is written as a capital, the entry of each complete theme (Abcd) may be clearly seen.

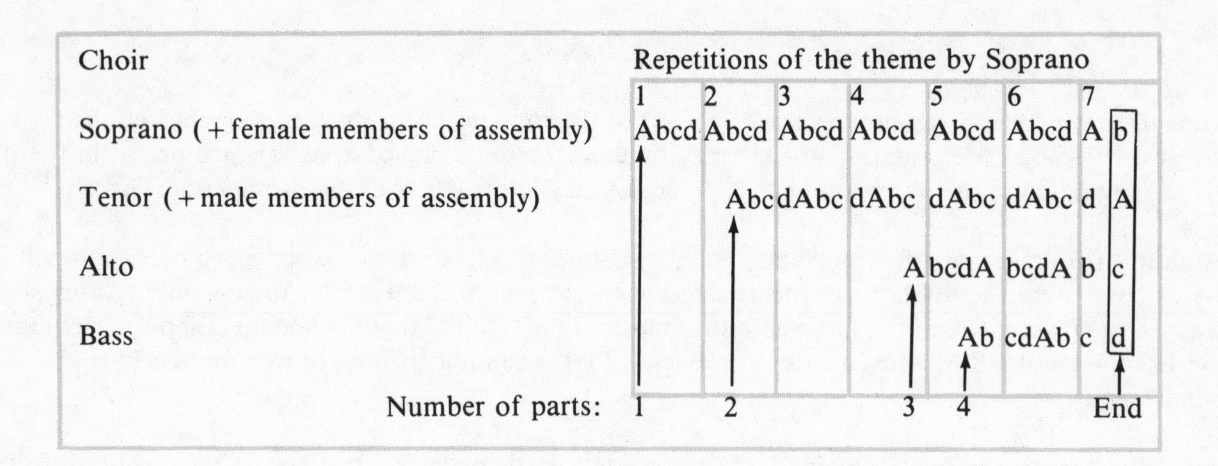

For conducting the singing, this succession is put into a diagram wherein each number corresponds to a repetition of the theme by the sopranos:

1	Unison (Soprano)
2	Unison, then two-part canon (Tenor entry at *b* of Soprano)
3	Two-part canon
4	Two-part canon, then three-part (Alto entry at *d* of Soprano)
5	Three-part canon, then four-part (Bass entry at *c* of Soprano)
6	Four-part canon
7	Four-part canon concluding with *b* of the Soprano

Second example: ***Magnificat* in four-voice canon with choir and instruments**

A reasonably large choir is needed to take the role of the choir in the previous example, namely, of supporting the assembly in its two-part canon, and completing the canon in four voices. In addition, a small choral group will sing the special passages for mixed voices. A number of good instrumentalists will also be needed.

The grid indicating all these elements, involving a more complex combination of forces, is easier to draw up if the succession of harmonic units is given in a vertical column on the far left, with the various forces shown in subsequent columns ordered from left to right according to their entry. One possible example, among others, is given below.

This grid gives a clear picture of the development of the piece: an instrumental introduction, the main theme sung by the sopranos, and then taken up in canon. When this has become well established in four voices, the second theme in *chorale* form is sung by the small choral group in unison with trumpet. The trumpet then develops the chorale in a special countermelody while the small group moves to a joyous and rhythmic passage. A natural *crescendo* is produced, reinforced by the trombone, and the conclusion is reached with a sustained climactic G major chord.

Succession of harmonic units	Keyboard - organ or other instrument	Cello	Flutes	Small choir	Large choir S	B	T	A	Tpt.	Tbn.
1	①	sequence								
2	②	[1]	sequence							
3	1	[2]	[2]							
4	2									
5	1	[3]			A					
6	2			sequence	b					
7	1	[4]	[3]	[1]	c					
8	2				d					
9	↓	↓			A					
10			[4]	[1]	b	A				
11					c	b				
12					d	c		A		
13					A	d		b		
14			[5]	[1]	b	A		c		
15					c	b	A	d		
16					d	c	b	A		
17	and so on	and so on	TACET	Chorale	A	d	c	b	Sequence [1]	
18	to the end	to the end		in unison	↓	A	d	c	(chorale with	
19	↓	↓		(2nd theme)		↓	A	d	small choir)	
20							↓	A		
21								↓	sequence	
22				sequence					[2]	
23				[2]					complete	
24										
25										①
26	↓	↓		sequence						②
27	1	sequence		[2]	↓	↓	↓	↓		③
28	2	[2]			d	c	b	A		④

The conducting diagram would be as follows:

1 to 4	Instruments. Flutes use sequence 2
5 to 8	Small choir: sequence 1. Large choir: canon theme Abcd (soprano)
9	Soprano: Repeat A
10 & 11	Bass: Begin canon theme as second voice Ab
12	Alto: Begin canon theme as third voice A
13 to 16	Regular successive entries of the four-part canon: S-B-T-A
17 to 20	Small choir and Trumpet: second theme (chorale)
21 to 24	Small choir: sequence 2; Trumpet: sequence 2 (without repeats)
25 to 28	Trombone sequence
	Rallentando over the final two measures

This exhaustive explanation could give the impression that things are more difficult than in fact they are. Ability in handling all these elements soon comes, and a taste develops for devising versions that match the capabilities of each group. Among the different versions possible it is important to choose the one which corresponds to the particular situation (which varies greatly according to the place, the number of participants, and so on). Only then can this music be harmoniously integrated into the celebration.

TABLE OF CONTENTS

I. OSTINATO RESPONSES AND CHORALES

II. LITANIES AND OTHER TEXTS WITH REFRAINS

III. ACCLAMATIONS

This section is contained only in the Vocal Edition.

IV. CANONS

BEATI

Happy they who dwell in God's house.

Basic Accompaniments

Keyboard

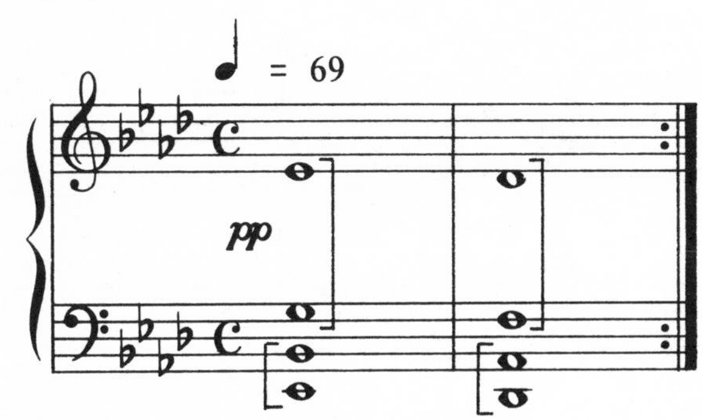

Guitar

Varied Accompaniments and Solos

Flute

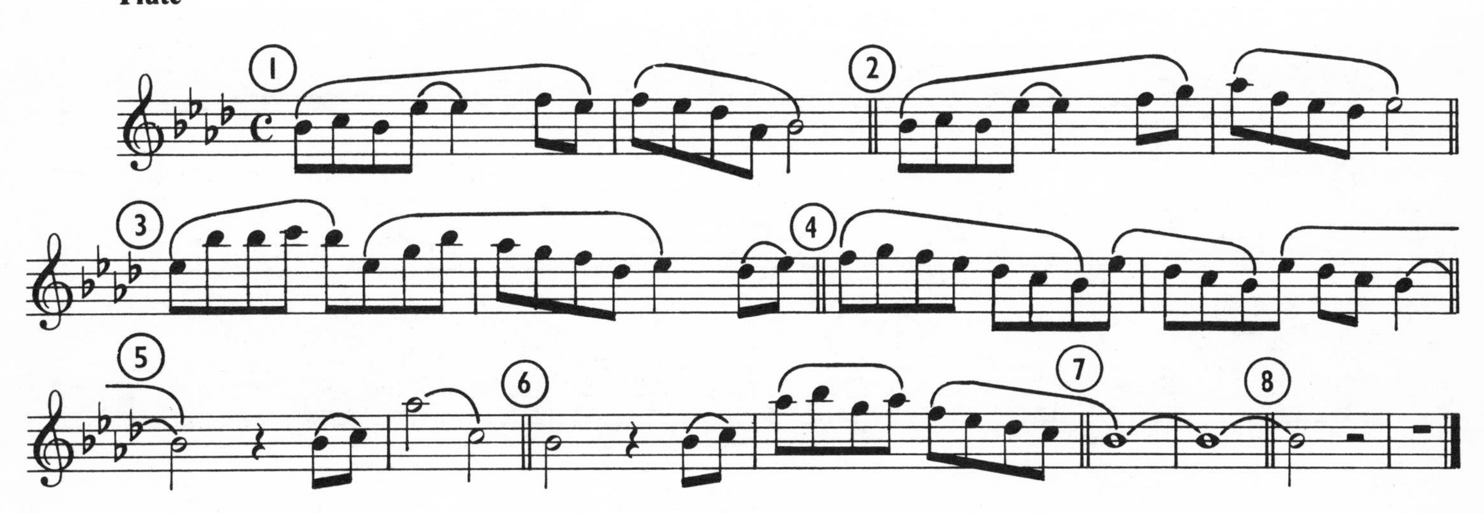

Oboe

English Horn

B♭ Clarinet

B♭ Trumpet

Trombone

Violin

Cello

BEATI PACIFICI

Blest are the peacemakers, and blest the pure in heart, for they shall see God.

Basic Accompaniment

Keyboard

Varied Accompaniments and Solos

Flute or Oboe

Legato

p

Oboe

1

2

B♭ Clarinet

3 3 3

3 3

3

3 3

B♭ Trumpet

CRUCEM TUAM

We adore your cross, O Lord, and we praise your resurrection.

Basic Accompaniment

Keyboard

Varied Accompaniments and Solos

Flute

Oboe or C Trumpet

B♭ Clarinet

1
2
(Fine)

B♭ Trumpet

1
(Choir: cru - cem tu -)
2

Trombone or Cello
1
2
(Fine)
1
2
2
(Fine)

GLORIA I

Glory to God in the highest.

Basic Accompaniment

Keyboard

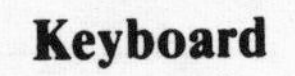

Varied Accompaniments and Solos

Various Instruments (Woodwinds or Strings)

B♭ Trumpet

HOW BLESSED ARE YOU

Basic Accompaniment

Varied Accompaniments and Solos

Flute

Violin

JESUS, REMEMBER ME

Basic Accompaniments

Keyboard

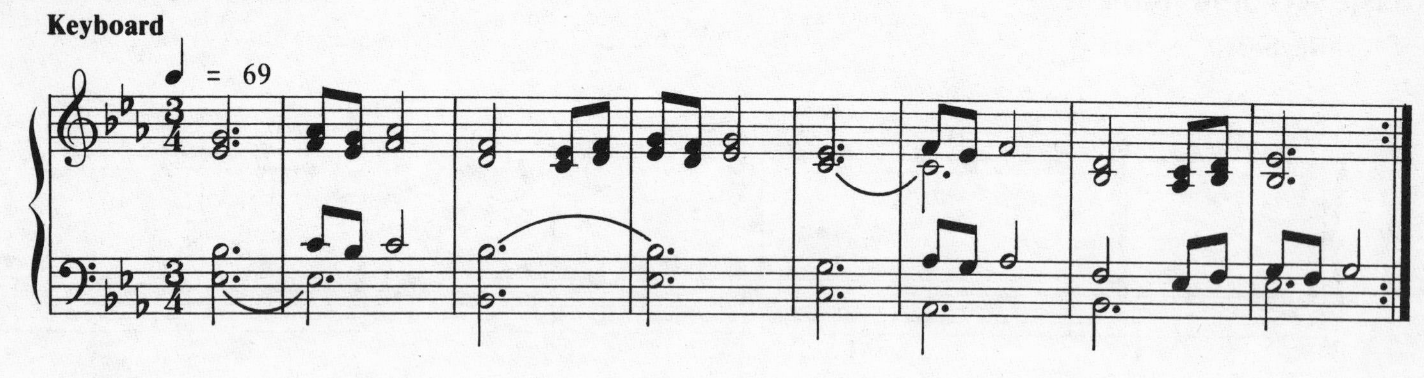

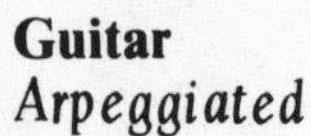

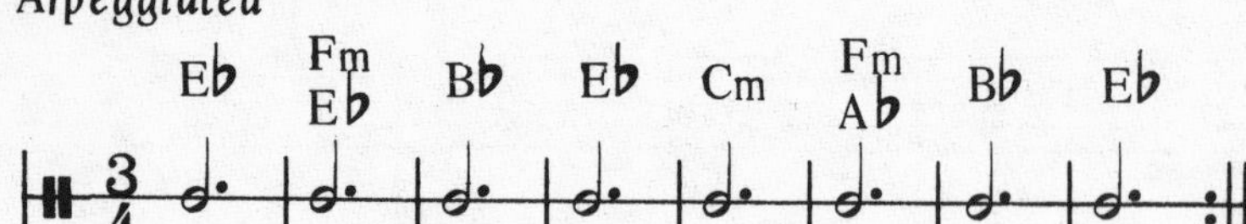

Varied Accompaniments and Solos

Flute

B♭ Trumpet

LAUDATE DOMINUM

Praise the Lord, all you peoples.

Basic Accompaniment

Keyboard

Varied Accompaniments and Solos

Flute

Oboe

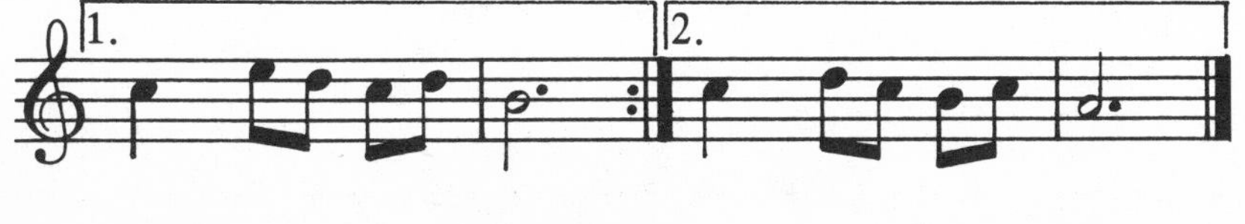

B^b Clarinet

B^b Trumpet

Trombone

LAUDATE OMNES GENTES

All peoples, praise the Lord.

Basic Accompaniment

Keyboard

Varied Accompaniments and Solos

Flute

Oboe

B^b Clarinet

B^b Trumpet

Trombone

MANDATUM NOVUM

I give you a new commandment, says the Lord: Love one another as I have loved you.

Basic Accompaniments

Keyboard or Instruments

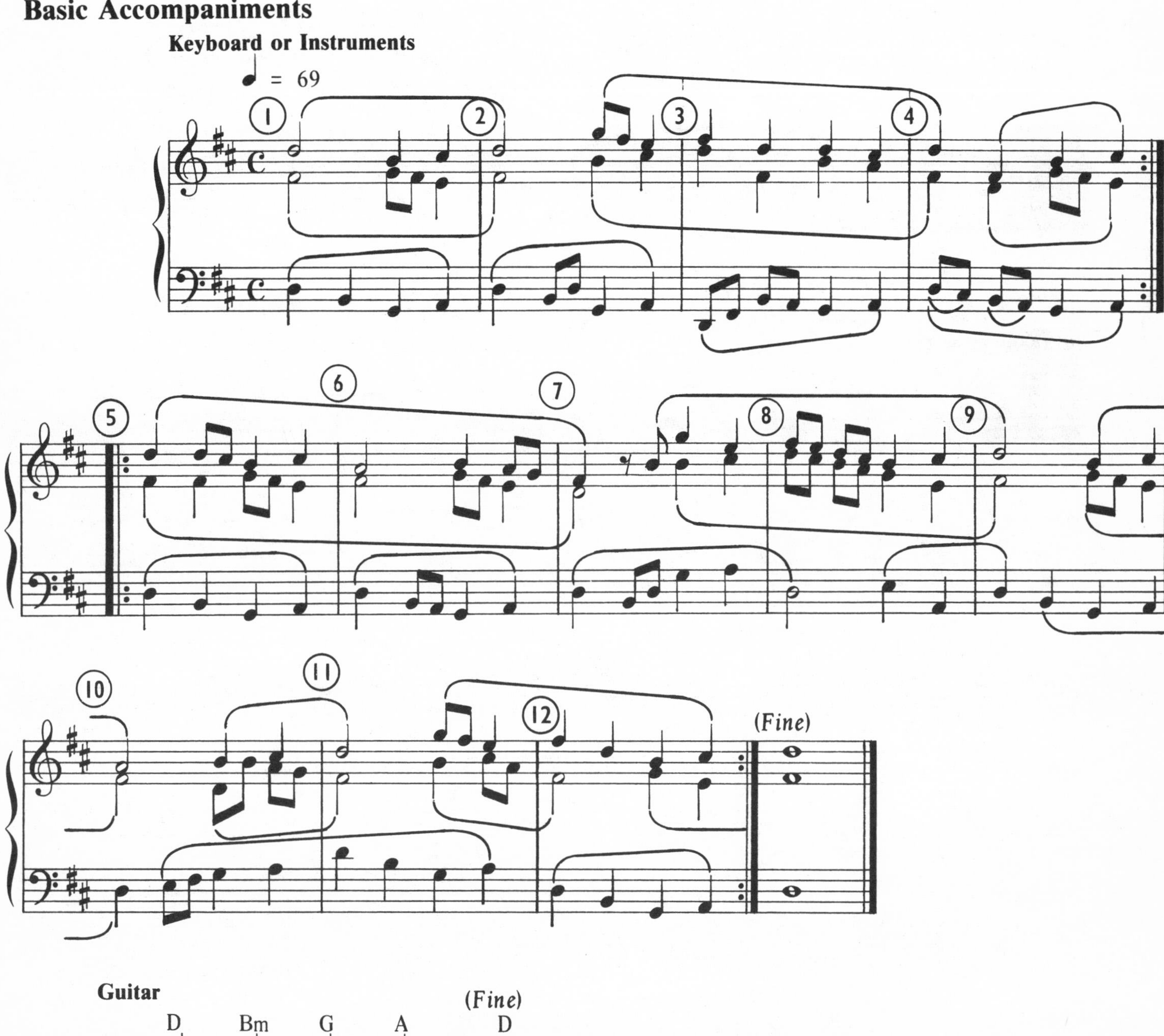

Guitar

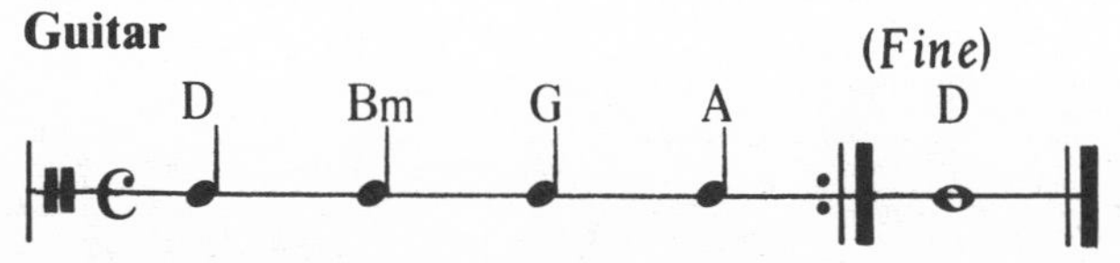

Varied Accompaniments and Solos

MISERERE MEI

Turn to me, have mercy on me, for I am alone and poor.

Cello

MISERERE NOBIS

Have mercy on us, O Lord.

Basic Accompaniments

Keyboard

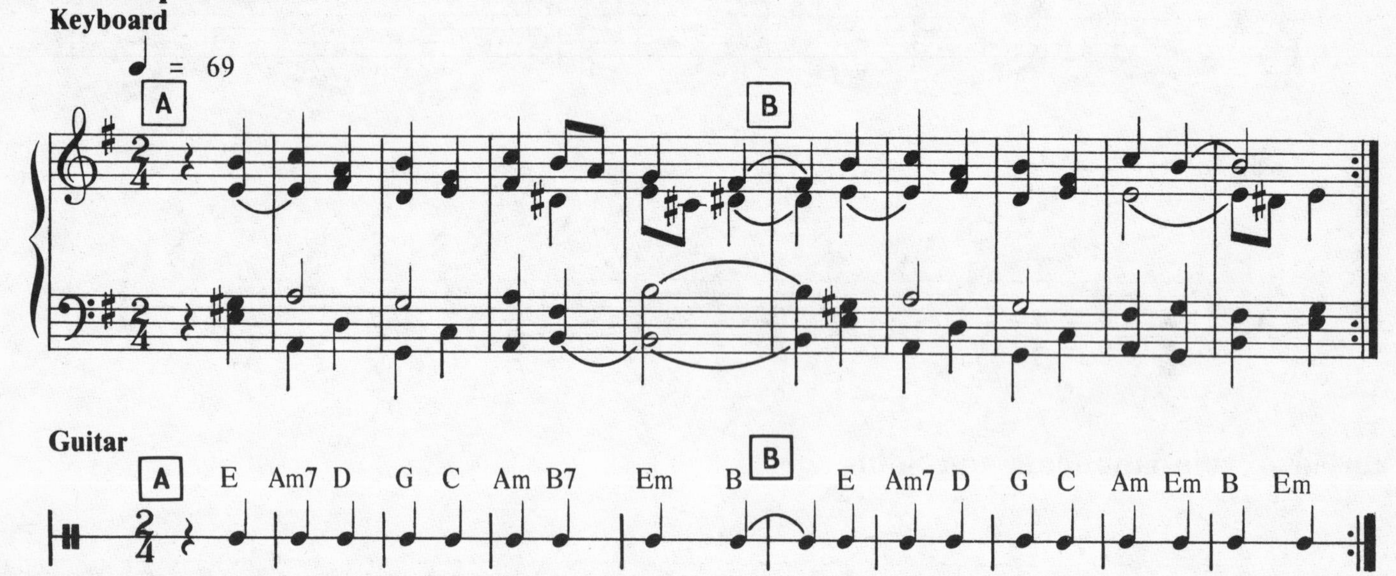

Varied Accompaniments and Solos

Flute

MISERICORDIAS DOMINI

For ever will I sing the mercy of the Lord.

Basic Accompaniments

Guitar

Arpeggiated

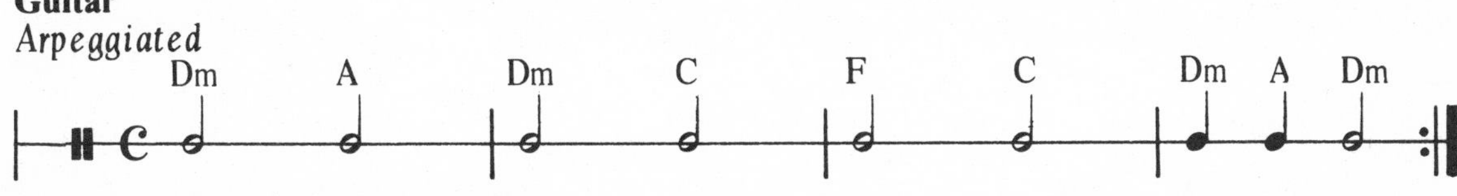

Varied Accompaniments and Solos

Oboe

B♭ Clarinet

B♭ Trumpet

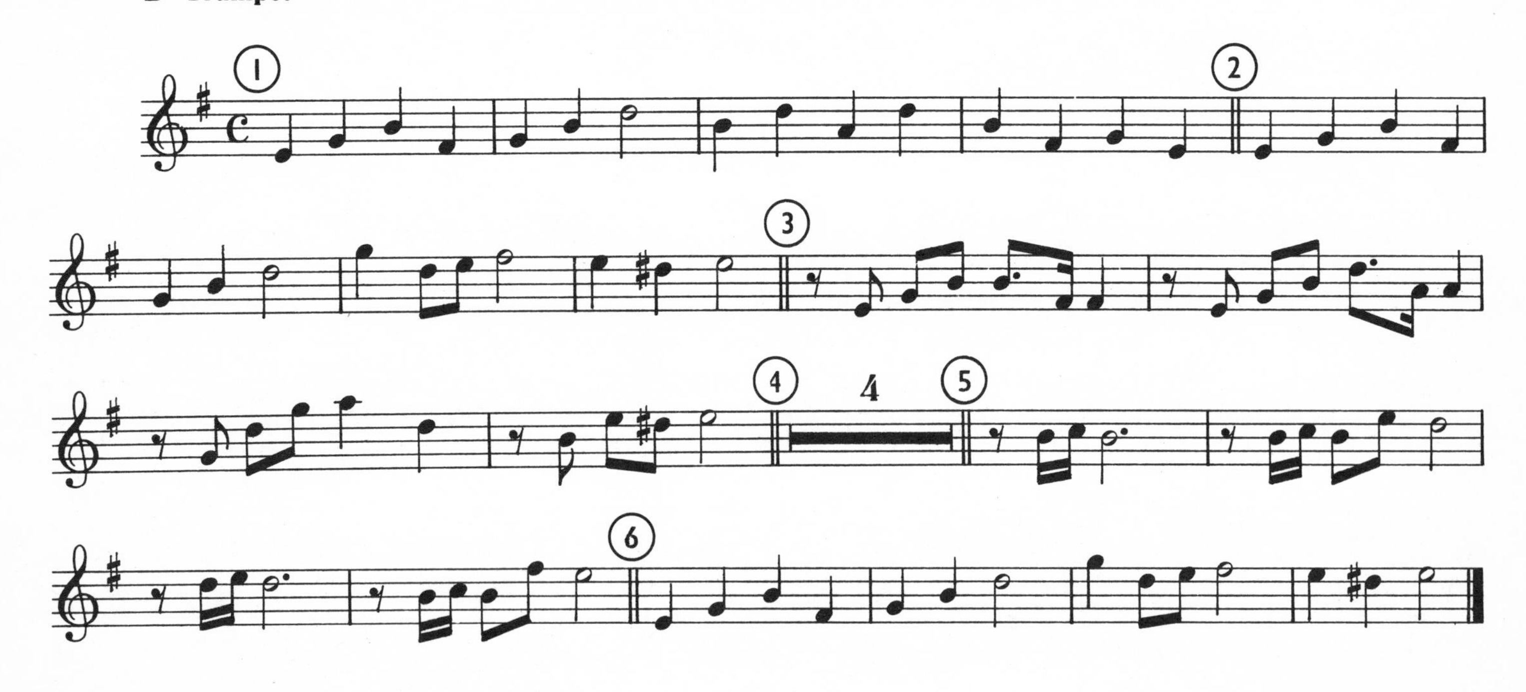

Trombone

Cello

Canticle of Simeon

NUNC DIMITTIS

Now, Lord, you can let your servant go in peace according to your promise.

Basic Accompaniments

Keyboard

Guitar

Varied Accompaniments and Solos

Flute

Oboe

English Horn

B^{b} Clarinet

Violin

Lord's Prayer

PATER NOSTER

Basic Accompaniments

Keyboard

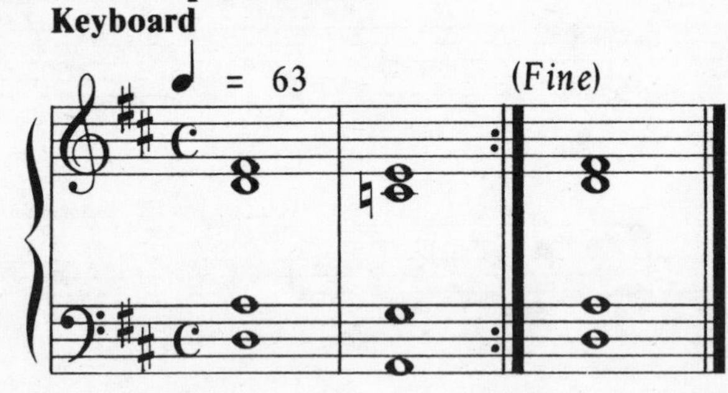

Guitar

Varied Accompaniments and Solos

Flute

Oboe

B^{b} Trumpet

Cello

Magnificat II

SANCTUM NOMEN DOMINI

My soul magnifies the holy name of the Lord.

Basic Accompaniment

Keyboard

Varied Accompaniments and Solos

Flute

Oboe

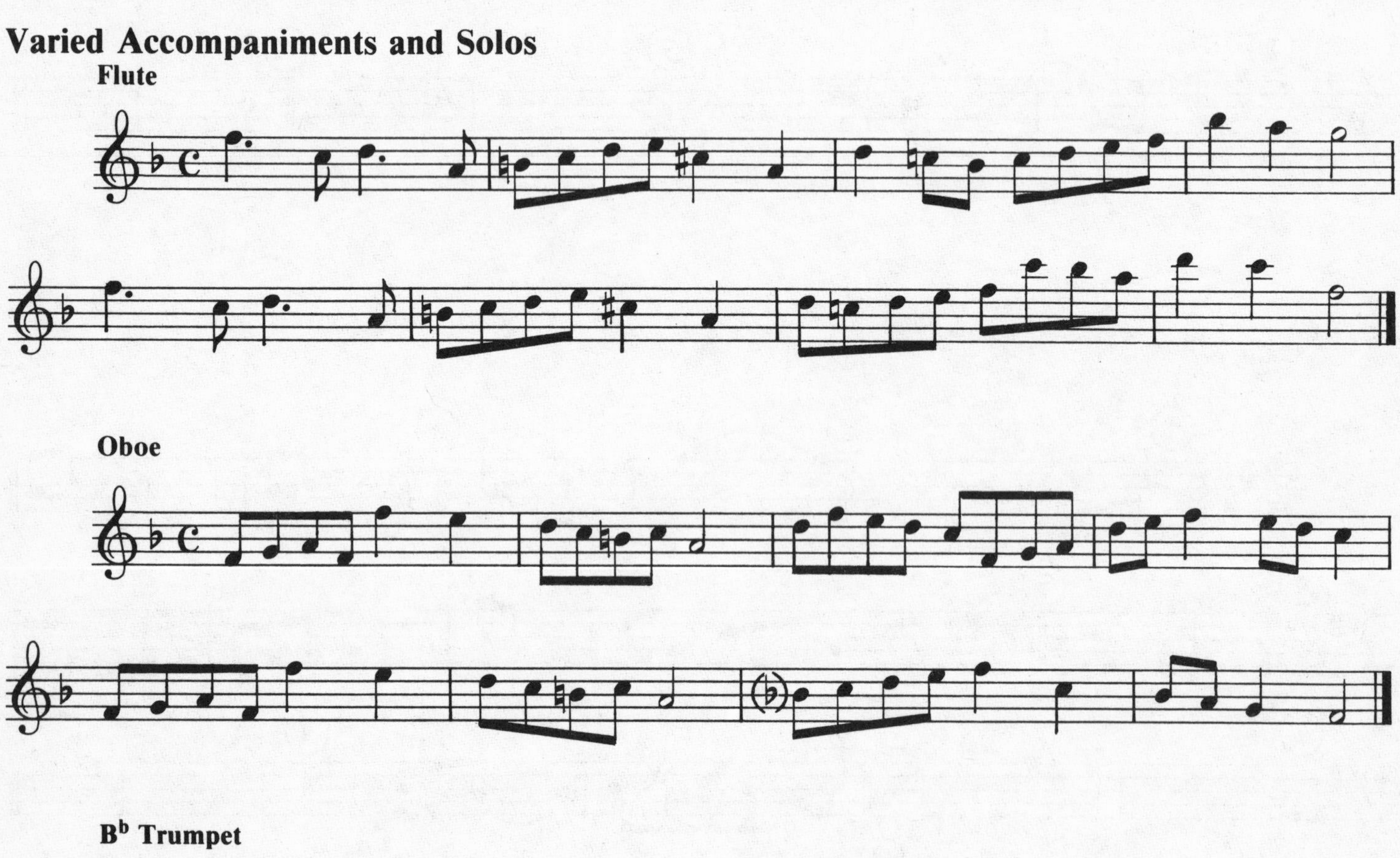

B♭ Trumpet

Cello

UBI CARITAS

Where charity and love are found, God himself is there.

Basic Accompaniments

Keyboard or Instruments

Guitar

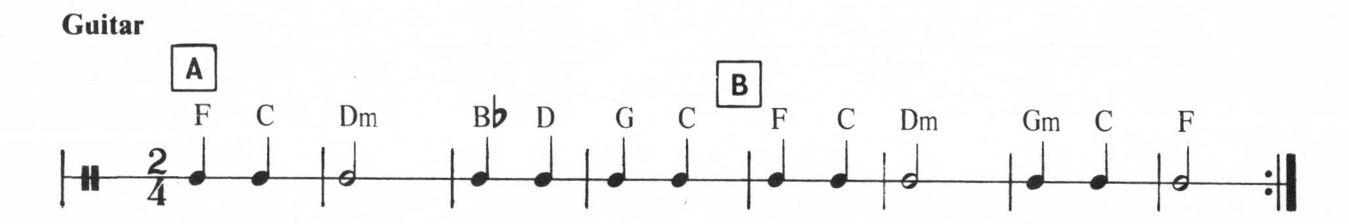

Bass or Cello (etc.)

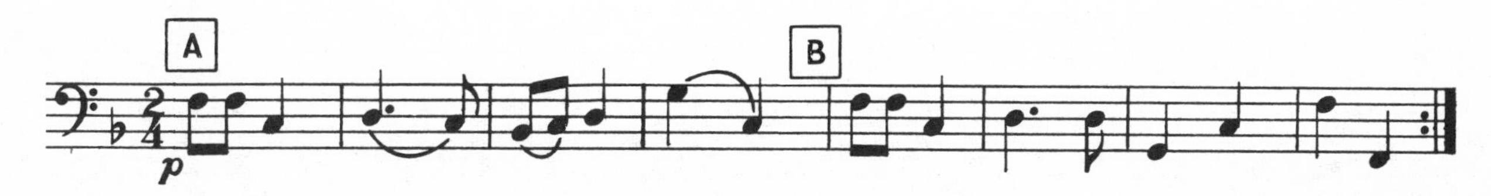

Varied Accompaniments and Solos

Flute

Oboe

B♭ Clarinet

B♭ Trumpet

Violin

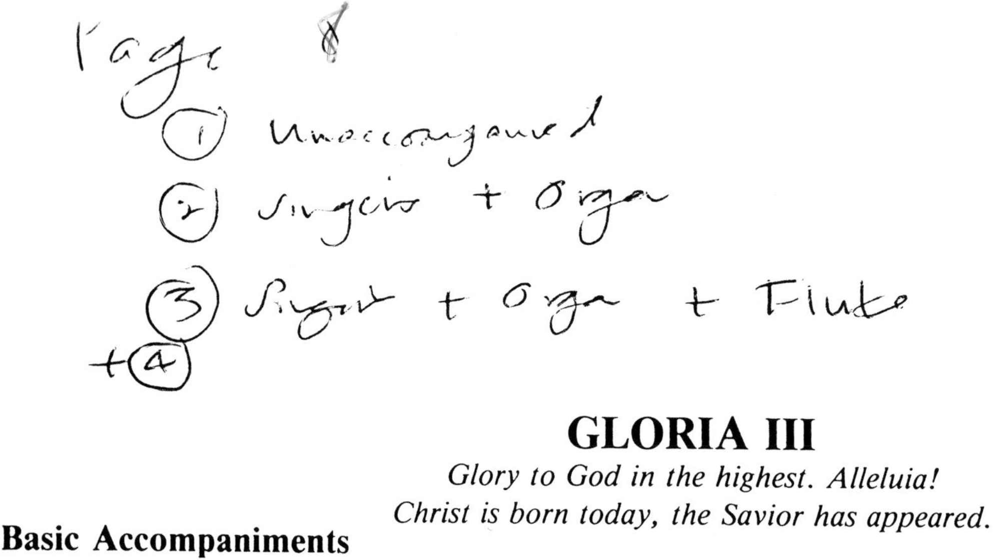

GLORIA III

Glory to God in the highest. Alleluia!
Christ is born today, the Savior has appeared.

Basic Accompaniments

Keyboard or Instruments

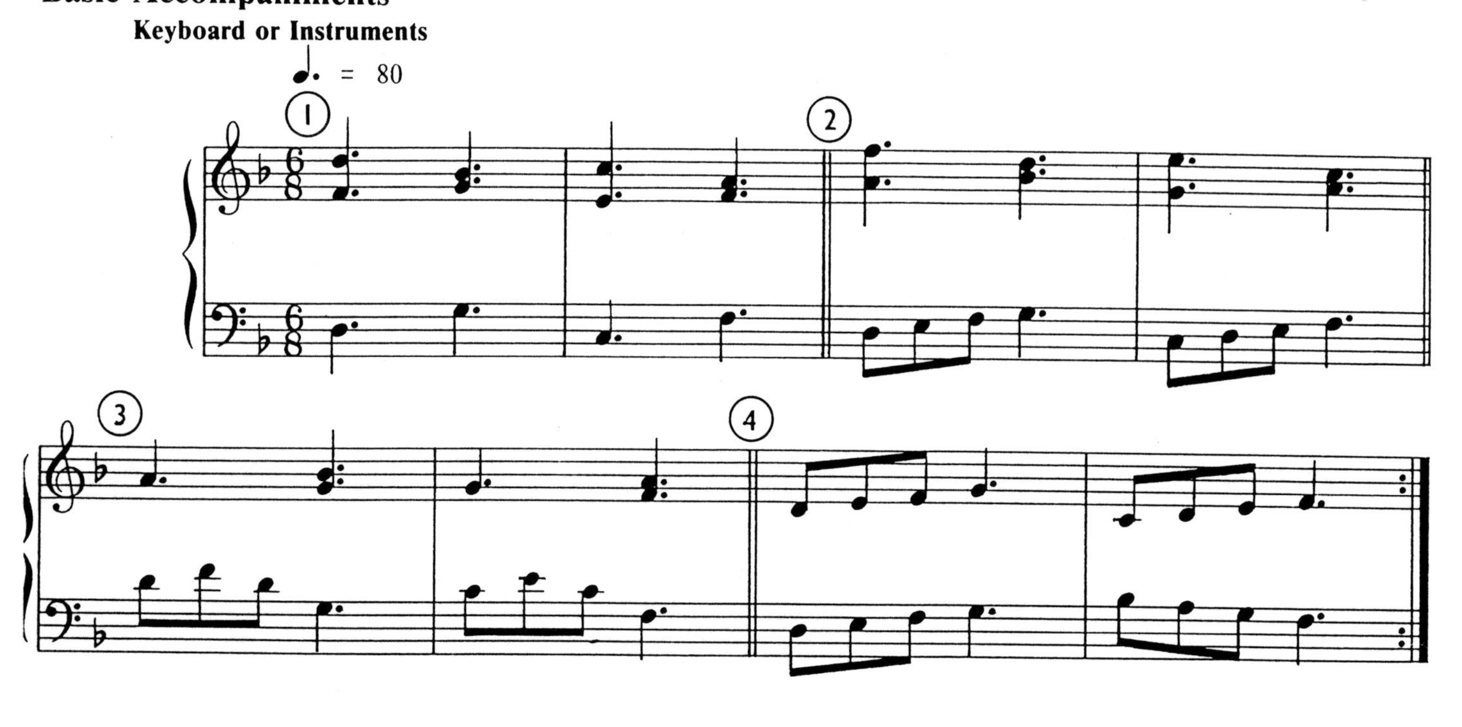

Varied Accompaniments and Solos

Flute or Oboe

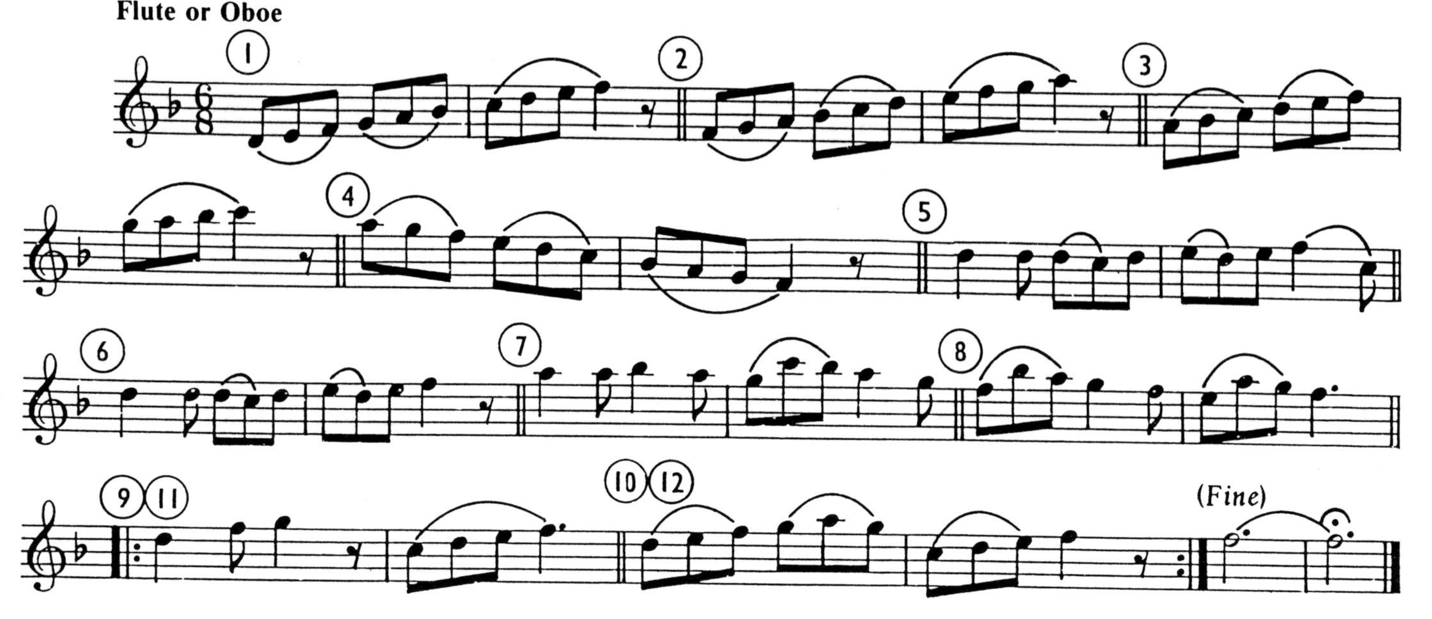

VENI SANCTE SPIRITUS

Come, Holy Spirit

Basic Accompaniments

Keyboard

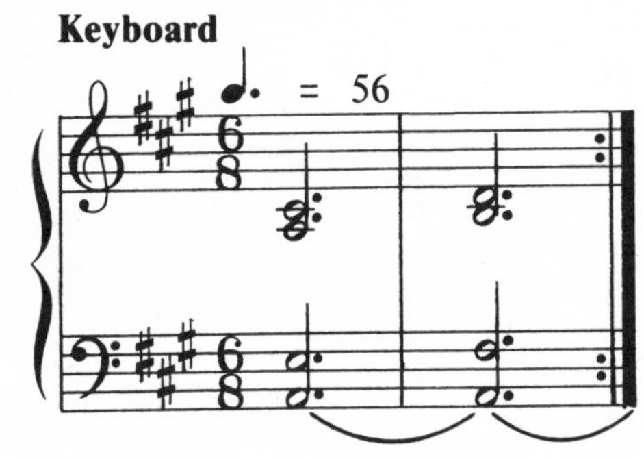

A to be held without interruption

Guitar

Varied Accompaniments and Solos

Flute

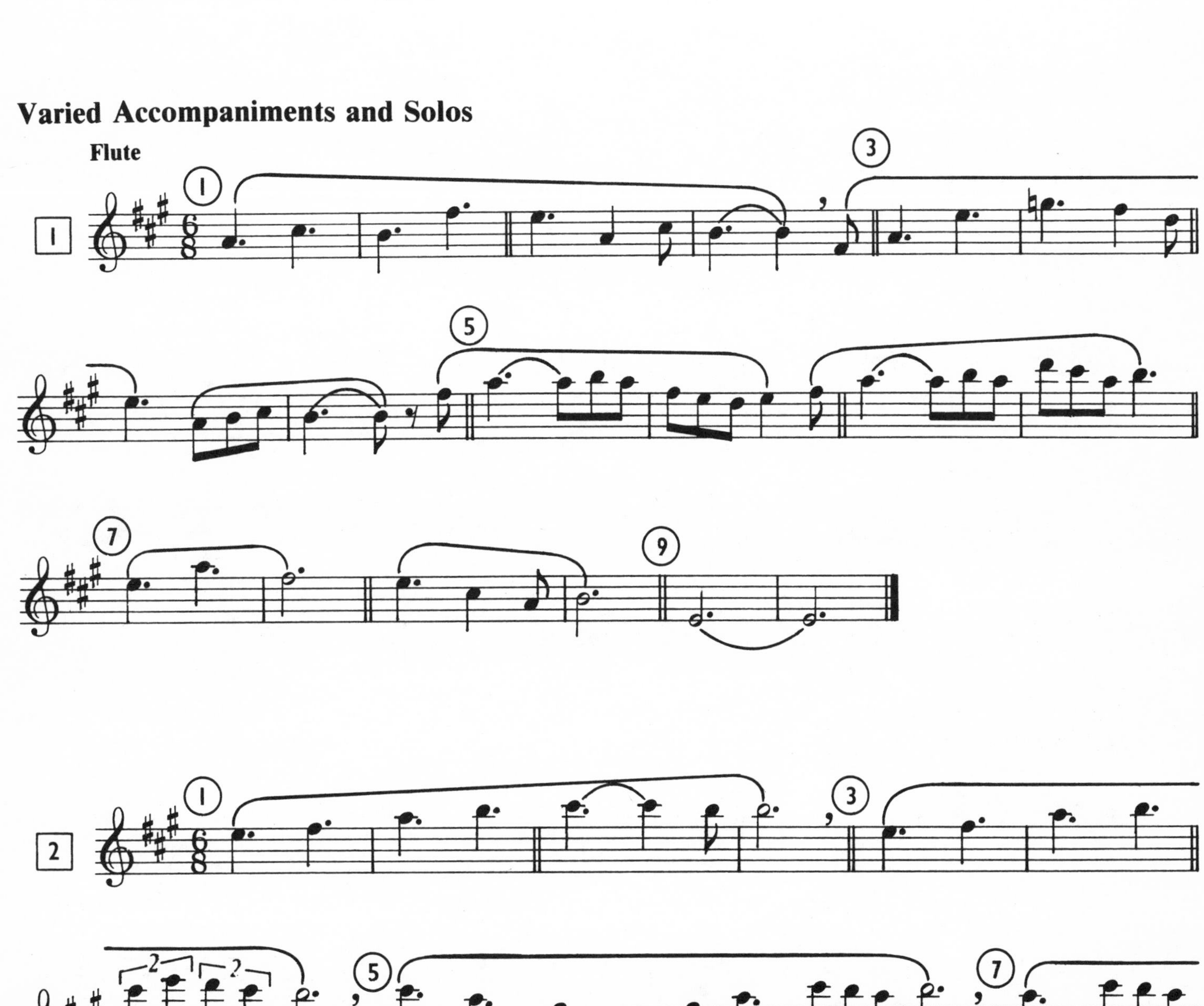

Oboe
(Veni)
English Horn
B♭ Clarinet

B♭ Trumpet

Trombone

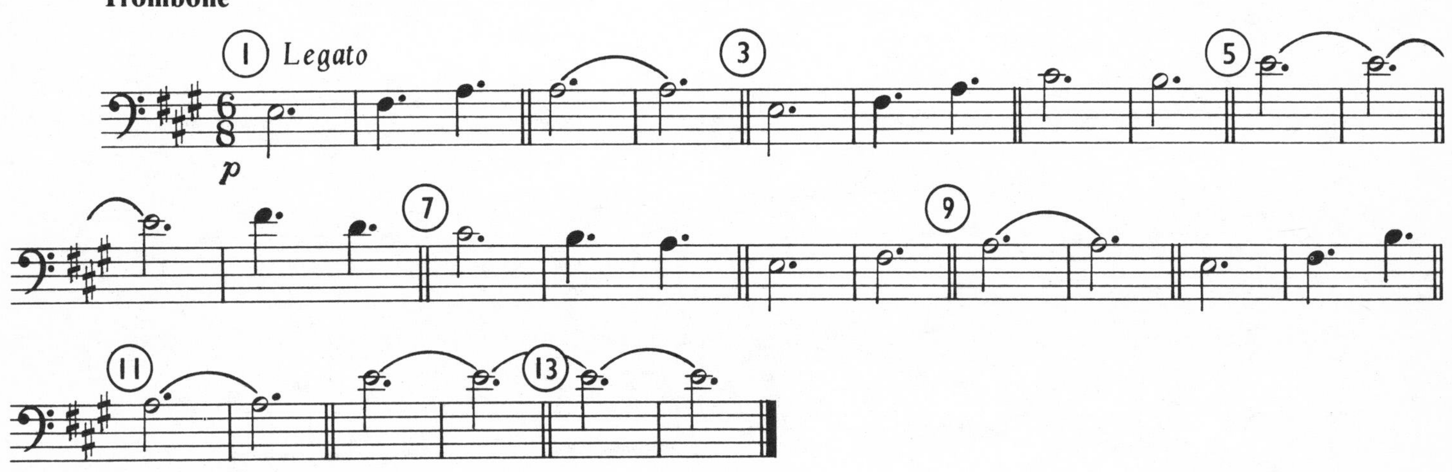

Cello

ADORAMUS TE DOMINE II — GLORIA

We adore you, O Lord. — Glory to God in the highest.

Basic Accompaniments

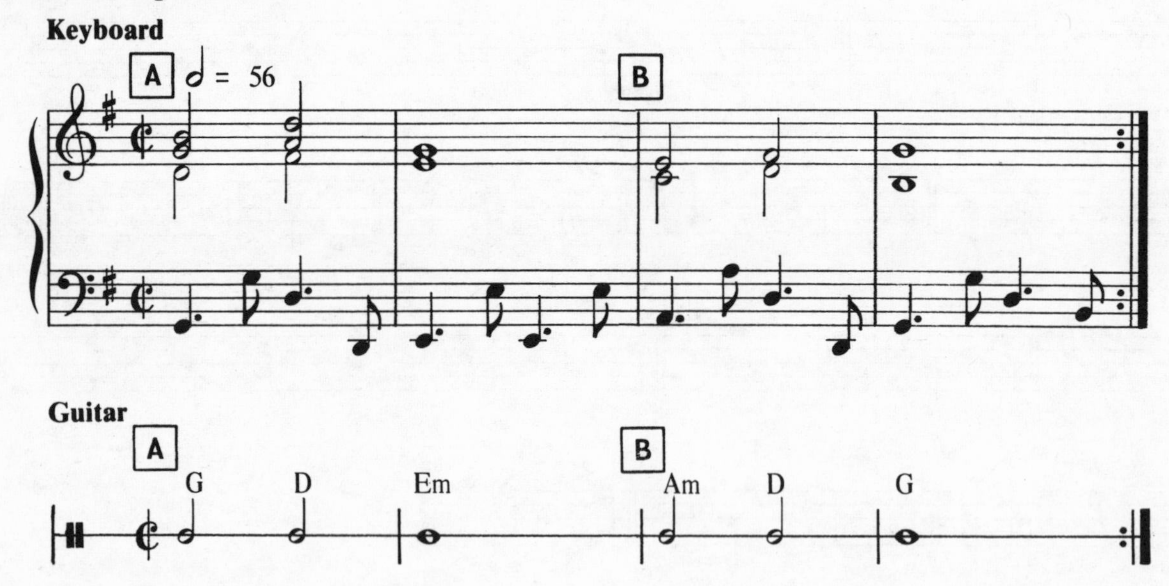

Varied Accompaniments and Solos

1.
2.

English Horn
1
2
3
4
5
6
B♭ Clarinet
1
2
3
4
5
6
1.
2.
7
8
1.
2.
B♭ Trumpet
1
1
2
p Legato
3
4

B♭ Trumpet

- with refrain "Gloria, Gloria"

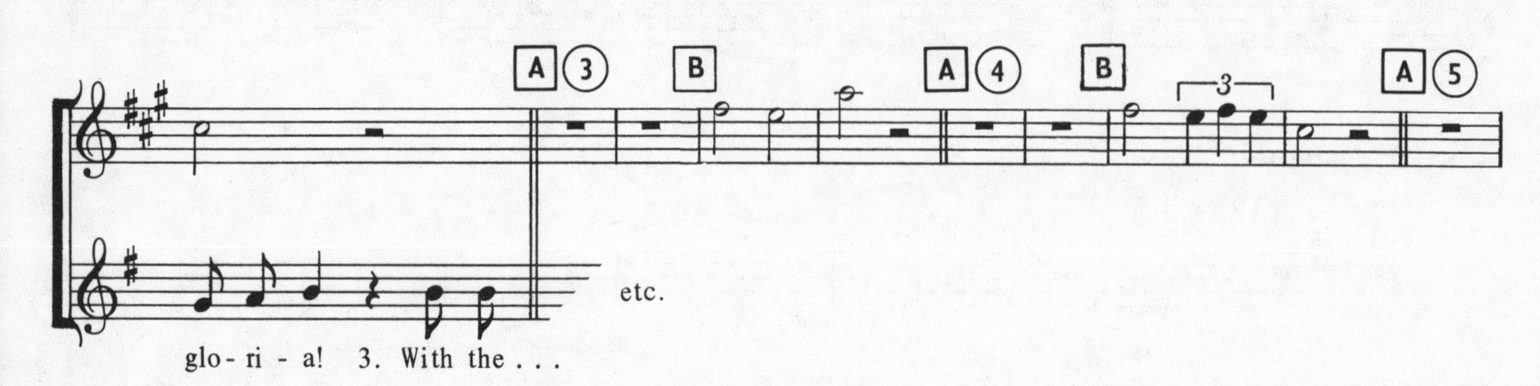

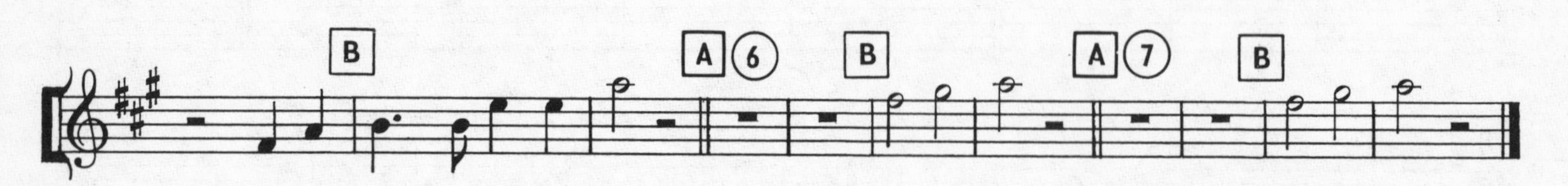

Trombone

EXAUDI NOS

Hear us

Basic Accompaniments

GLORIA TIBI DOMINE

Glory to you, O Lord.

Basic Accompaniments

Keyboard or Instruments

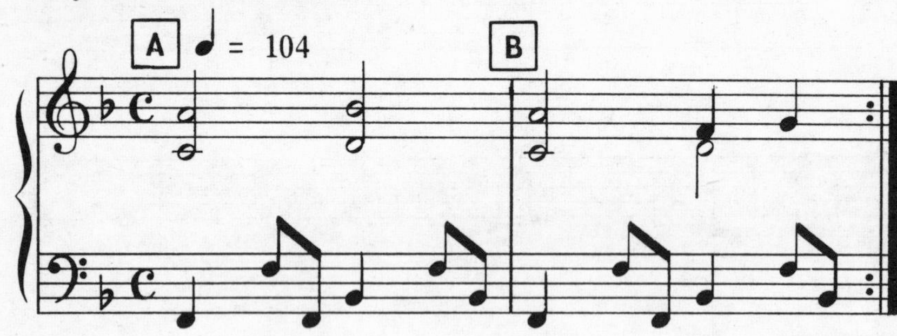

Guitar

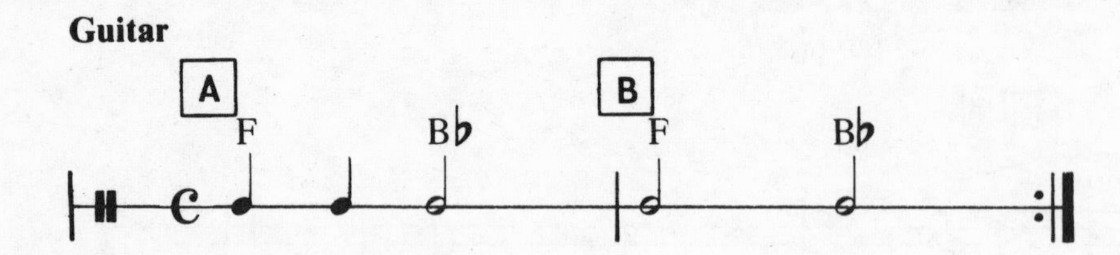

Varied Accompaniments and Solos

Flutes or Violins

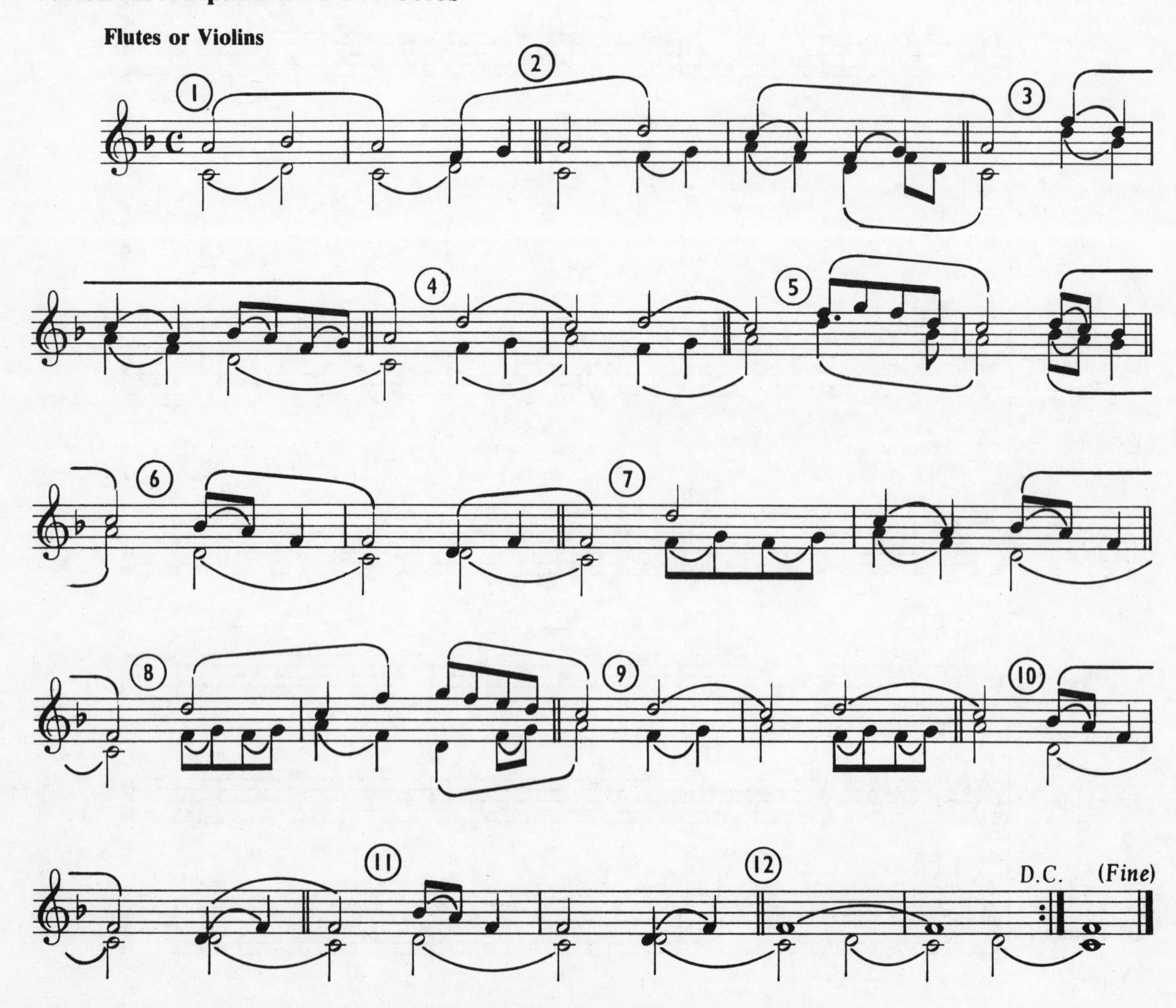

Oboe

B♭ Trumpet

1. With the refrain A

2. With the concluding Amens.

Solo or Duo with Trombone/Cello

Trombone or Cello

Timpani or Tom-Toms

JESU CHRISTE MISERERE

Jesus Christ have mercy on us.

Basic Accompaniments

Keyboard or Instruments

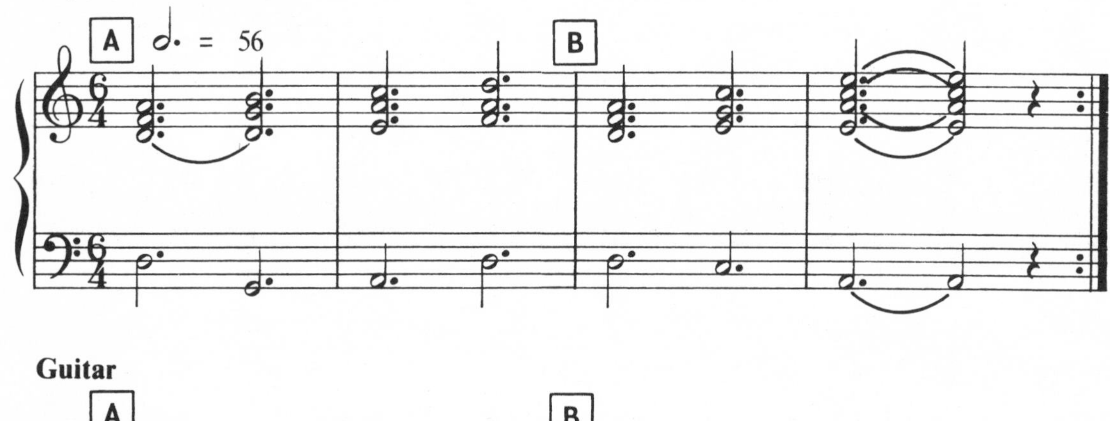

Guitar

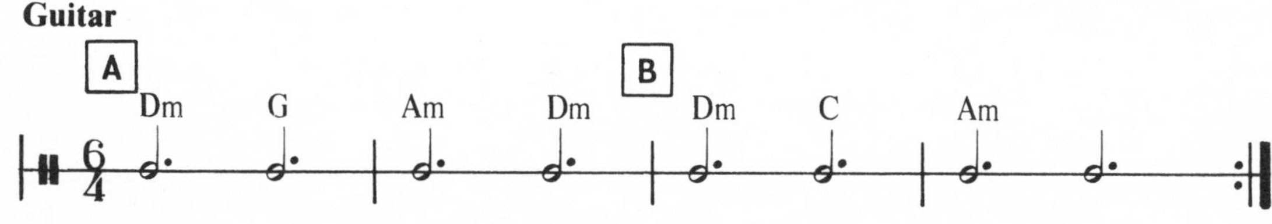

Gong

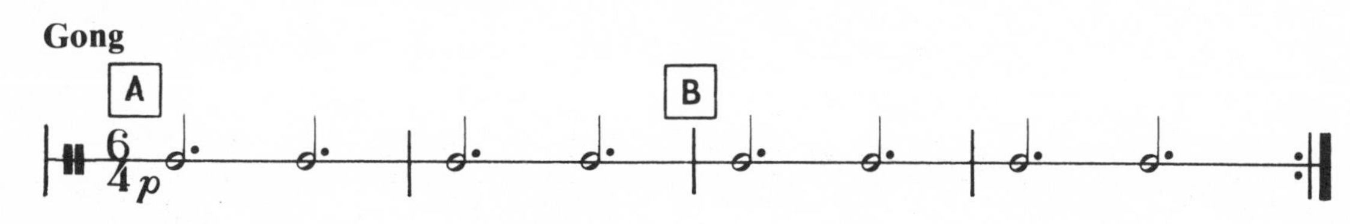

Varied Accompaniments and Solos

Flute

B♭ Trumpet

Violin

LIBERA NOS DOMINE

Deliver us, O Lord.

Basic Accompaniments

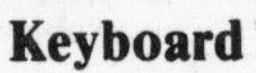

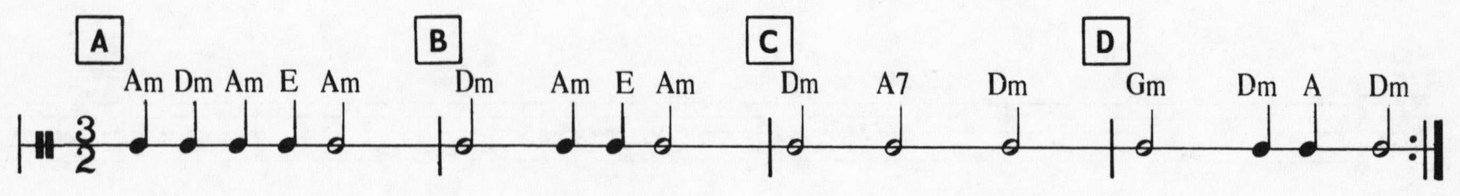

Varied Accompaniments and Solos

Flutes, Violins, etc.

B♭ Trumpet

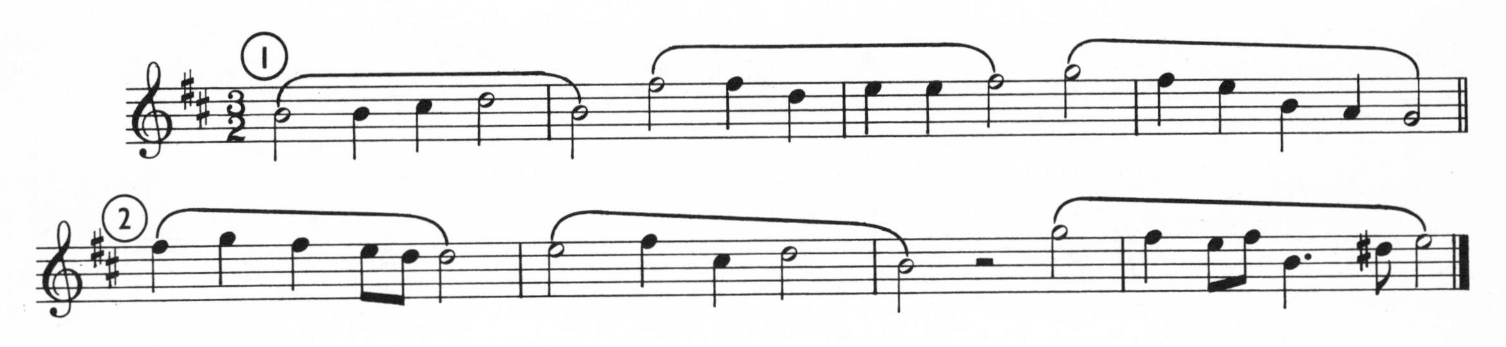

Bass or Cello

MARANATHA! ALLELUIA! I

Come soon! Alleluia!

Basic Accompaniments

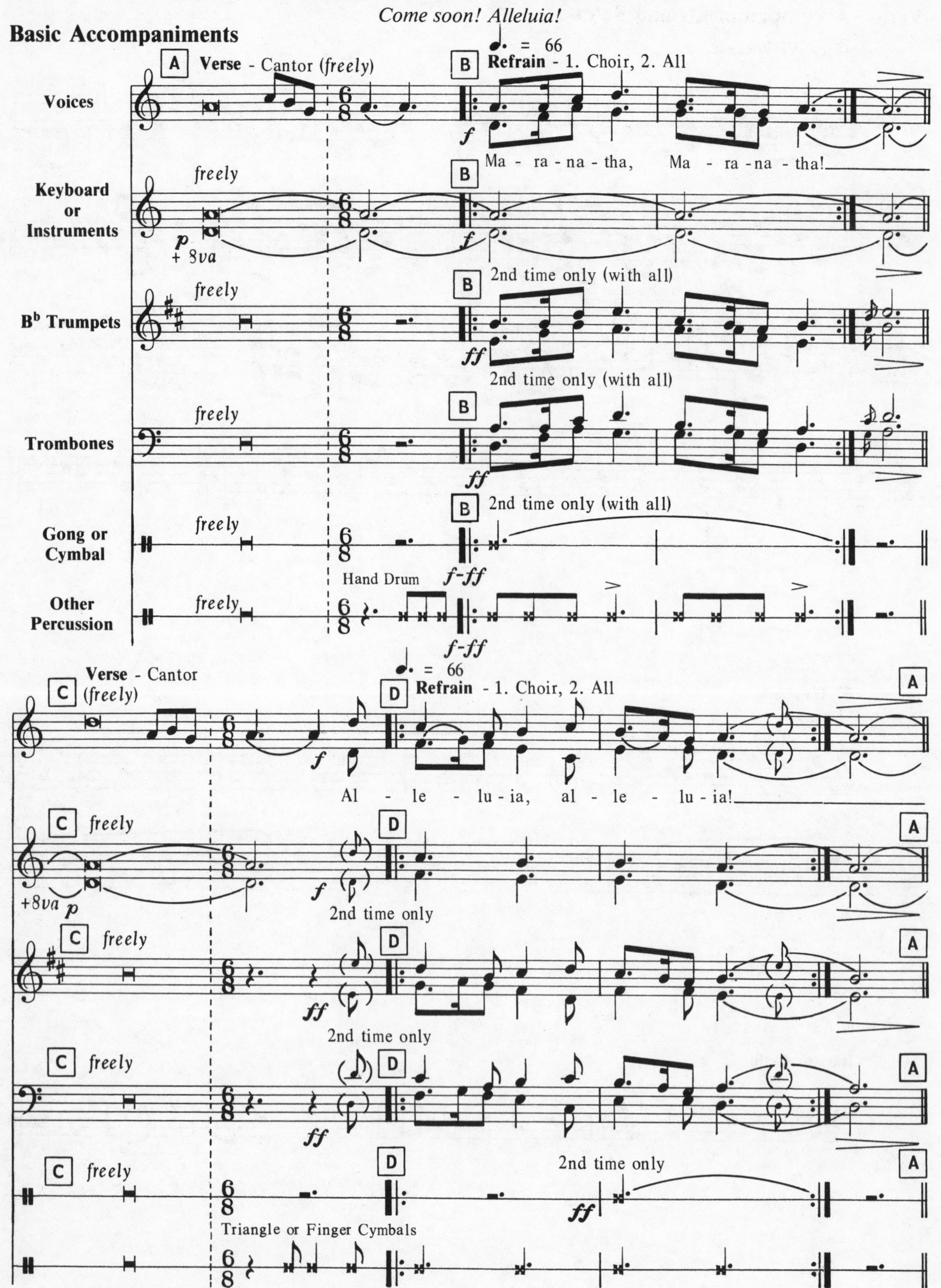

Varied Accompaniments - (full version)

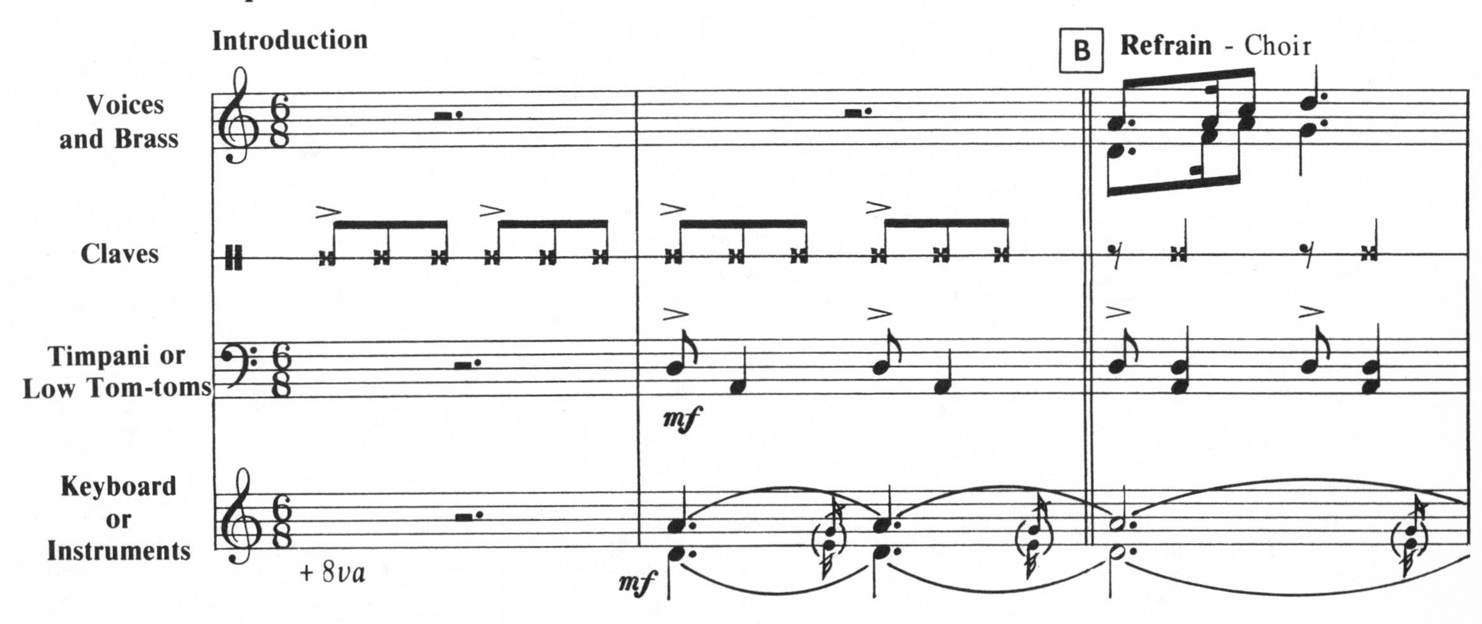

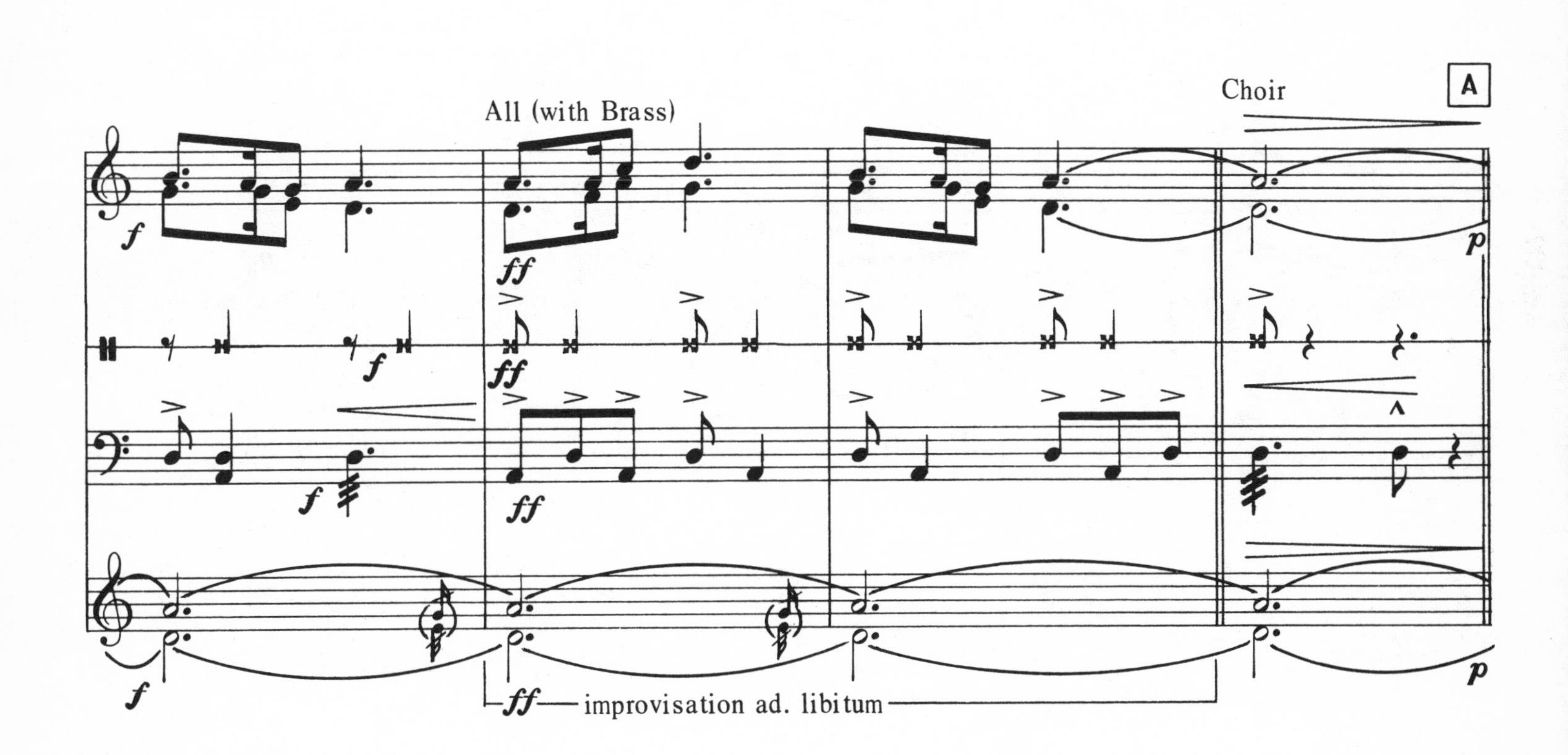

A and **B**

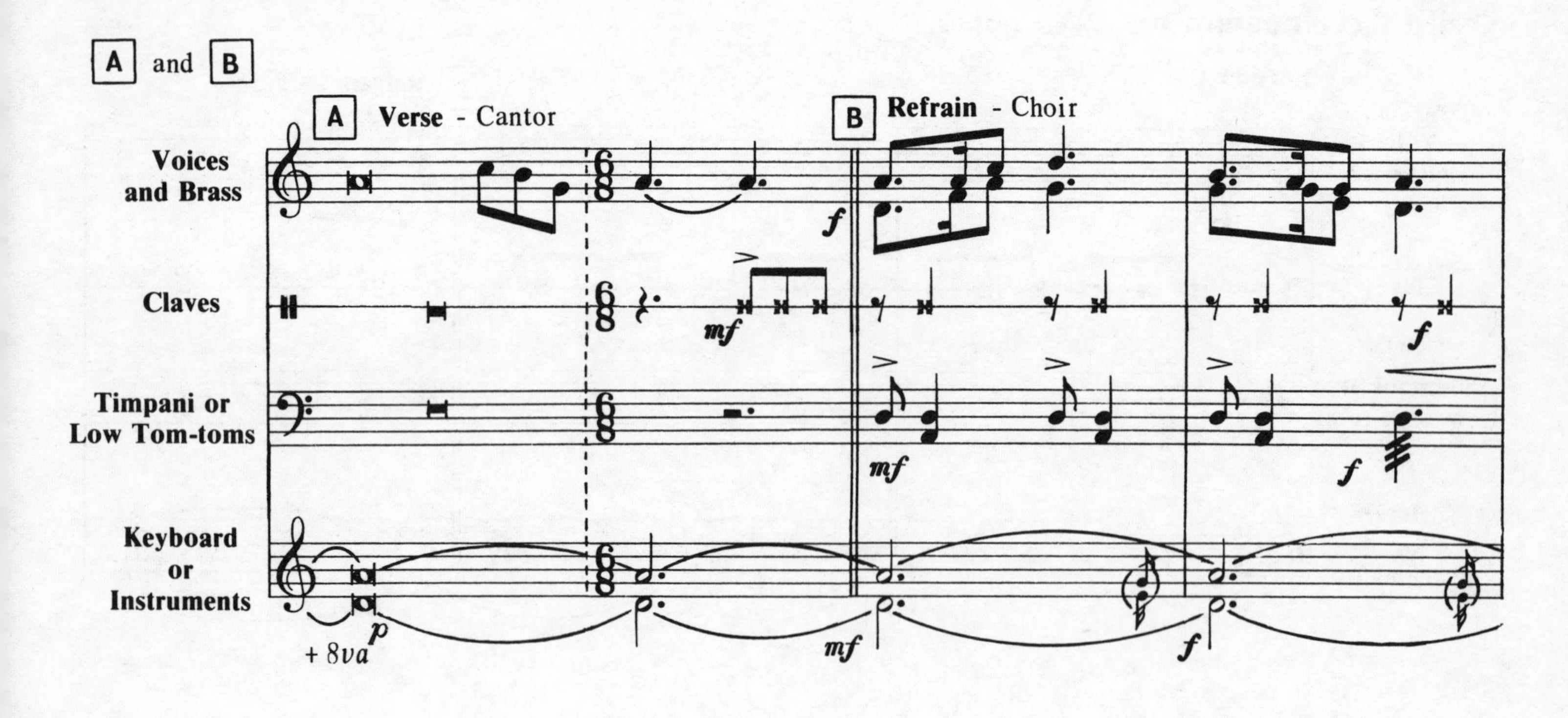
A
Verse - Cantor
B
Refrain - Choir
Voices and Brass
Claves
Timpani or Low Tom-toms
Keyboard or Instruments
+ 8va

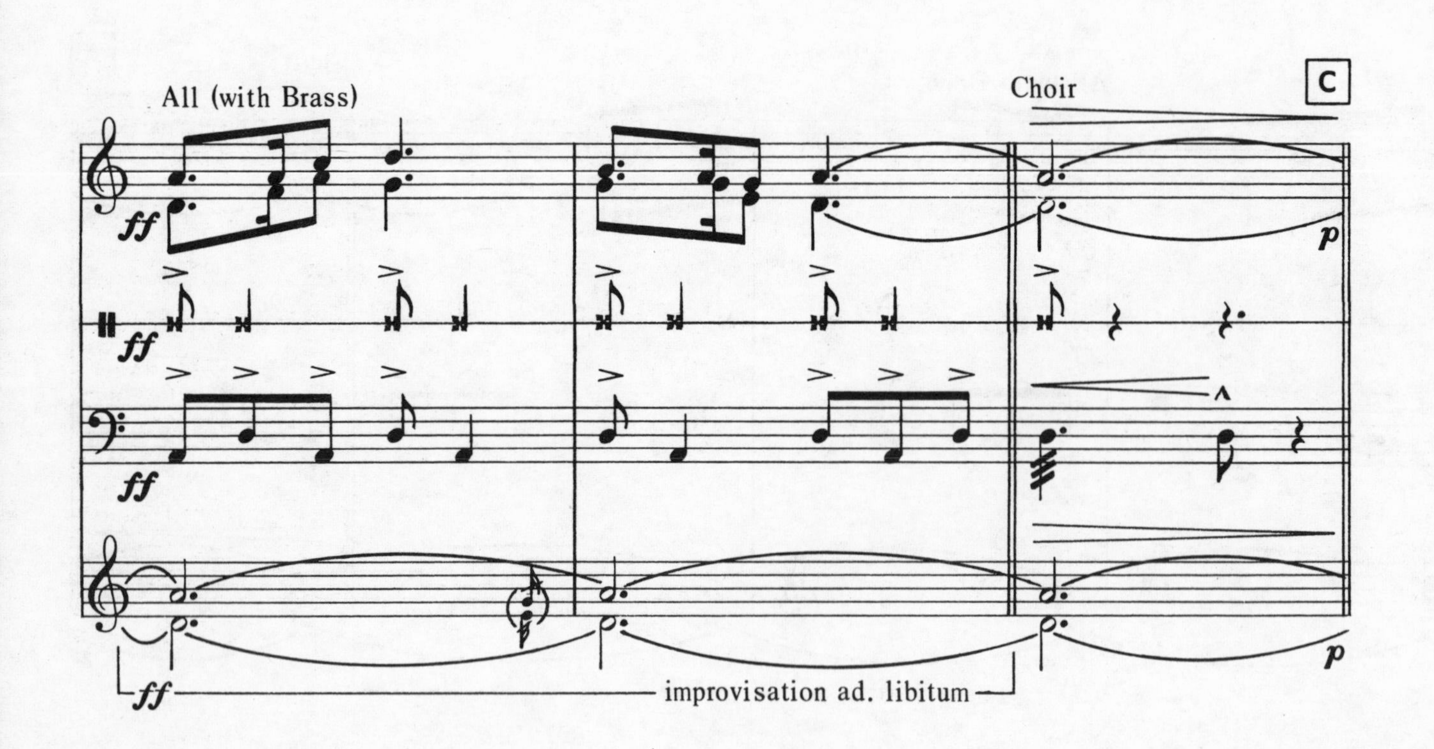
All (with Brass)
Choir
C
improvisation ad. libitum

C and D

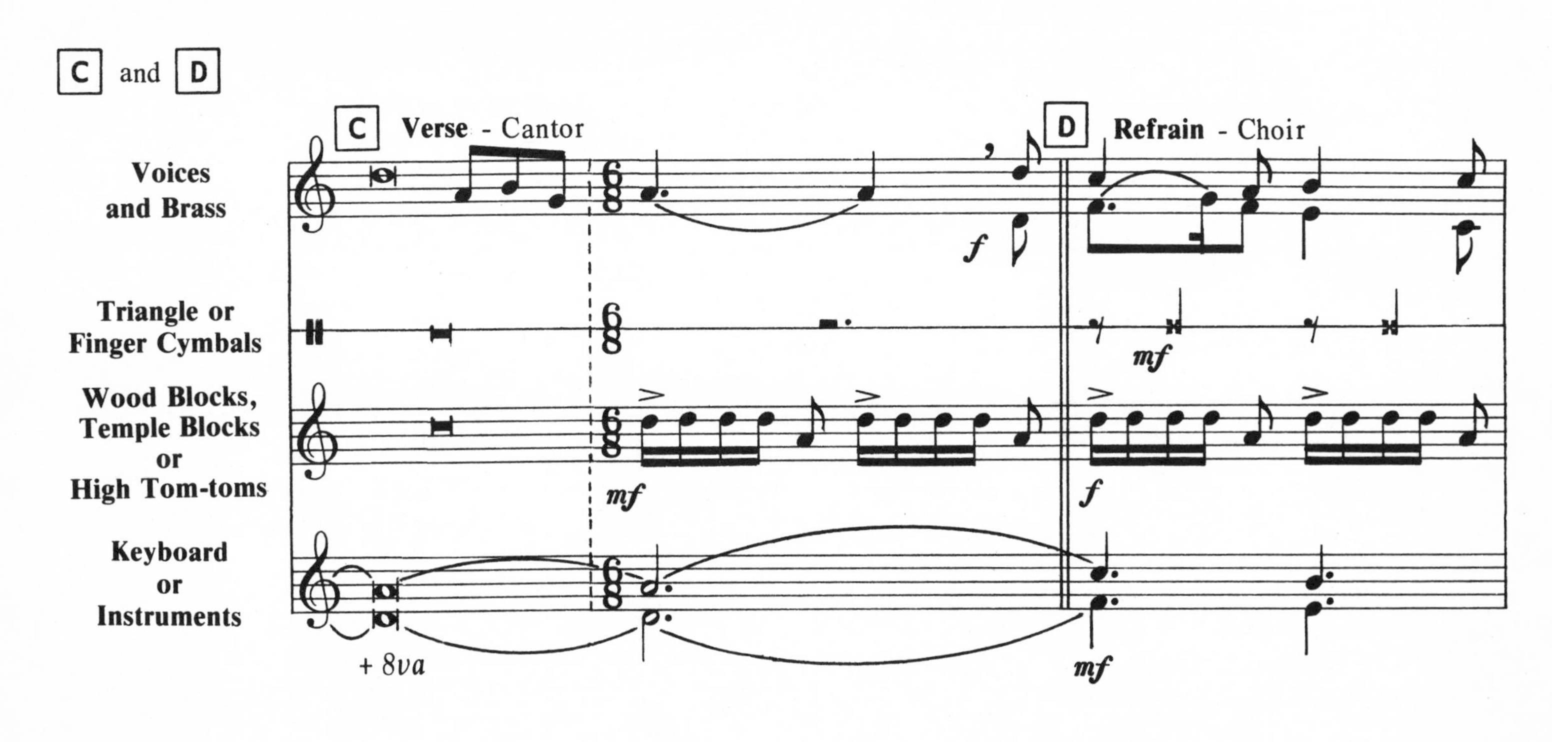
C
Verse - Cantor
D
Refrain - Choir
Voices
and Brass
Triangle or
Finger Cymbals
Wood Blocks,
Temple Blocks
or
High Tom-toms
Keyboard
or
Instruments
+ 8va

All (with Brass)
Choir
A

MEMENTO NOSTRI DOMINE

Remember us, O Lord.

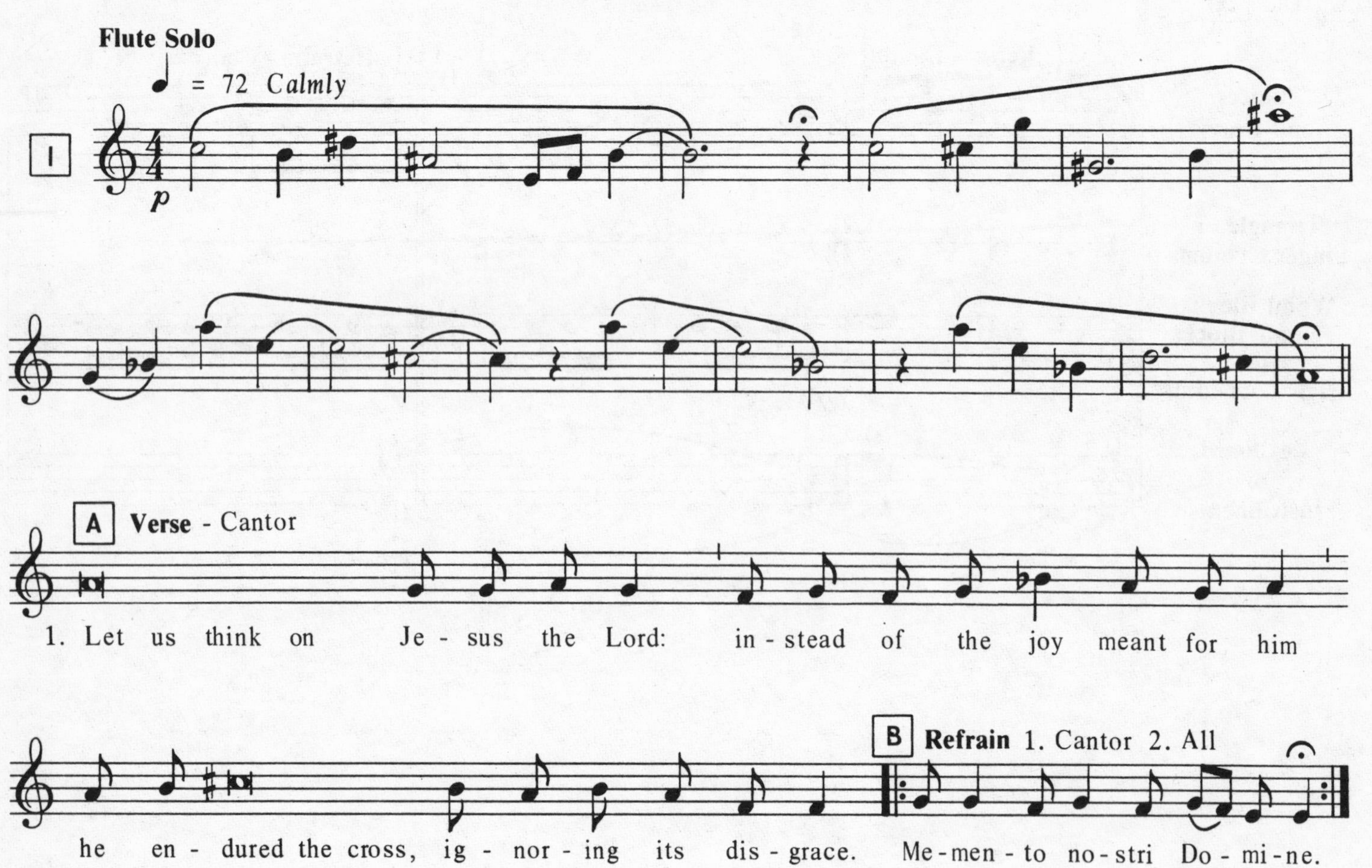

3. You lived among us, healing the sick, proclaiming the good news to the poor, and free-dom to pris-on-ers.

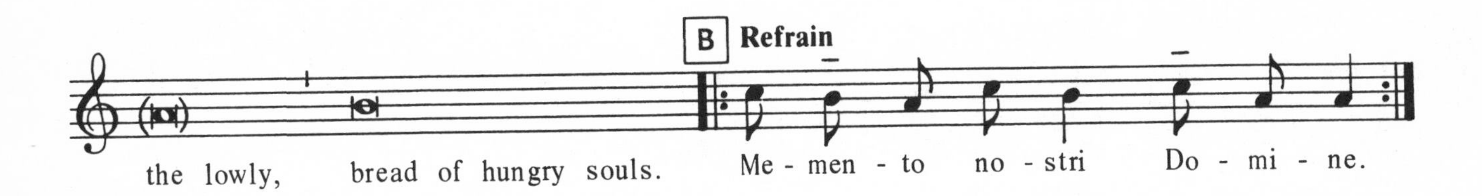

Flute Solo
Calmly
5
mf
f

very slow
A Verse
5. Je - sus, master of patience and good - ness, for - giv - ing all

B Refrain
who seek your mer - cy. Me - men - to no - stri Do - mi - ne.

Flute Solo
A little faster
6
mf

A Verse
6. Je - sus, gentle and hum - ble of heart, call - ing the wea - ry and the bur - dened.

B Refrain
Me - men - to no - stri Do - mi - ne.

Flute Solo
Calmly
7
p
A Verse
7. Jesus, you came into the world to serve and to lay down your life you had no-where to
lay your head, you were be-trayed for mon - ey, dragged before Pi - late and nailed to the cross.
B Refrain
Me - men - to no - stri Do - mi - ne.

Flute Solo
A little more movement
8
f
p (echo)
ff
A Verse
8. Je - sus, by your resurrection from the dead, you are
Lord of all the worlds, a - live for ever to intercede with your Fa-ther and ours.
B Refrain
Me - men - to
no - stri Do - mi - ne. Me-men-to no-stri Do - mi-ne. Me-men-to no-stri Do - mi - ne.

TE ROGAMUS AUDI NOS

We ask you to hear us.

Basic Accompaniments

Keyboard or Instruments

Guitar

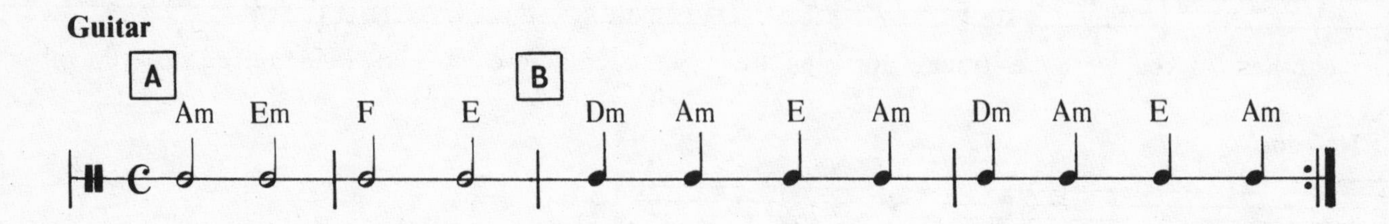

Varied Accompaniments and Solos

Flute

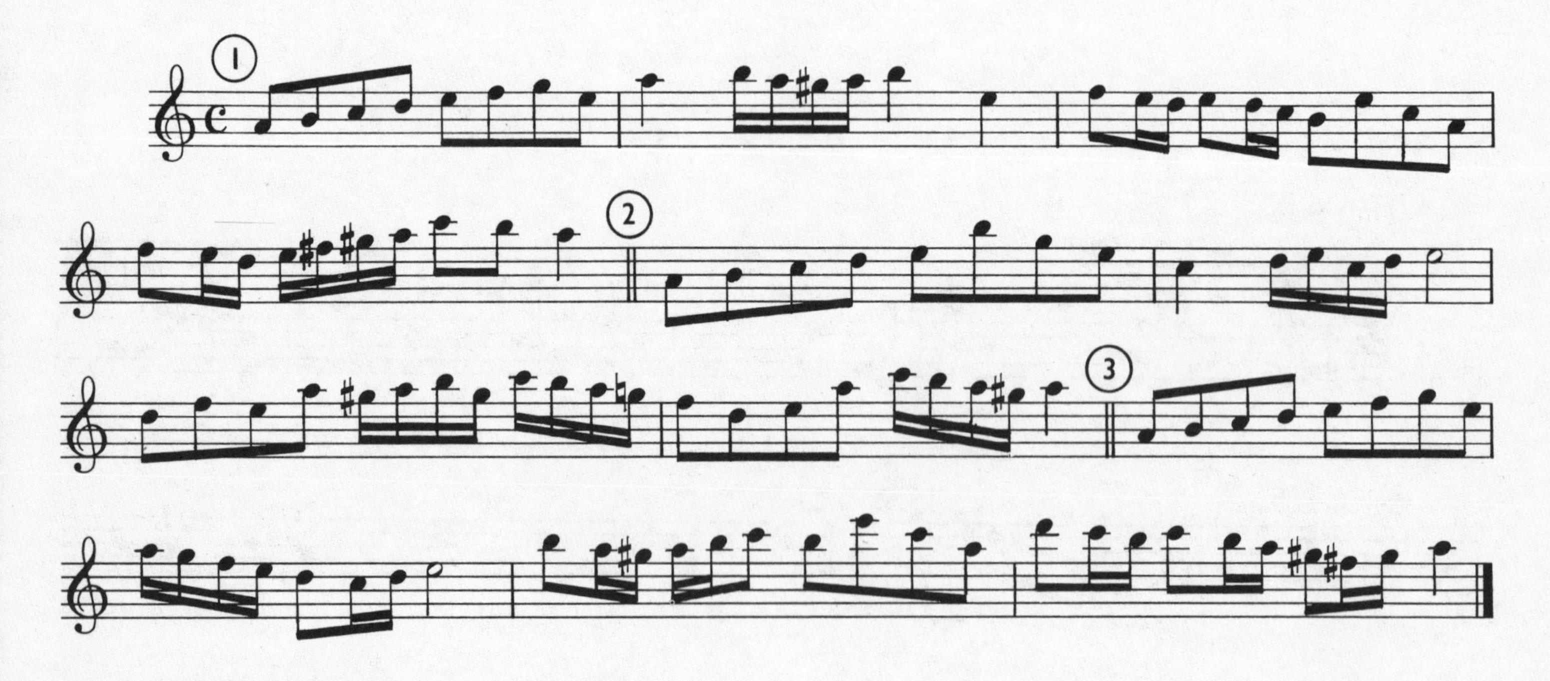

Oboe

3
B♭ Clarinet
1
2
B♭ Trumpet
1
2
Cello
1
2

VENI CREATOR SPIRITUS

Come, Creator Spirit

Basic Accompaniments

Varied Accompaniments and Solos

Flute
1
2
3
4
5
6
7
8
9
10
11
12
p
13
14
B♭ Trumpets
1 Legato
p
2
3
mf
4
Trombone
p
mf
5
3
f
3
3
f
6
3
7
8
9
mf
mf
10
p
p
11

Violin
1
2
3
4
5
6
7
8
9
8va
10
11
12
13
14
15
16
17
18
Cello
1
2
3
4
5
6
7
9
10
11
12
13
14
15
16
17
18
19
20

Percussion

Timpani or Tom-Toms

Finger Cymbals or Triangle

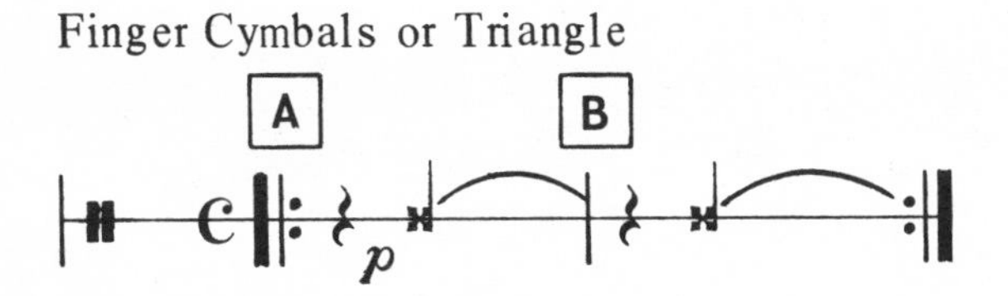

Gong or Cymbal

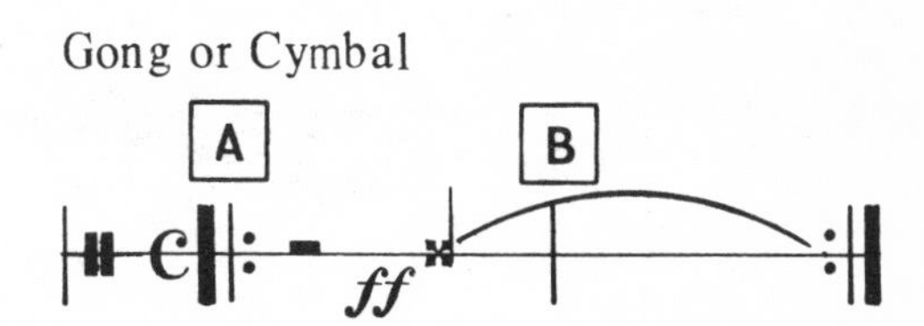

AGNUS DEI

Lamb of God, you take away the sins of the world, have mercy on us; grant us peace.

Basic Accompaniments

Keyboard

Guitar

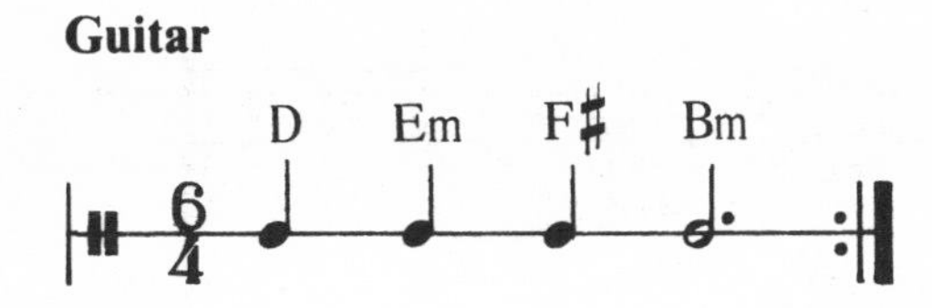

Varied Accompaniments and Solos

Flute and Oboe

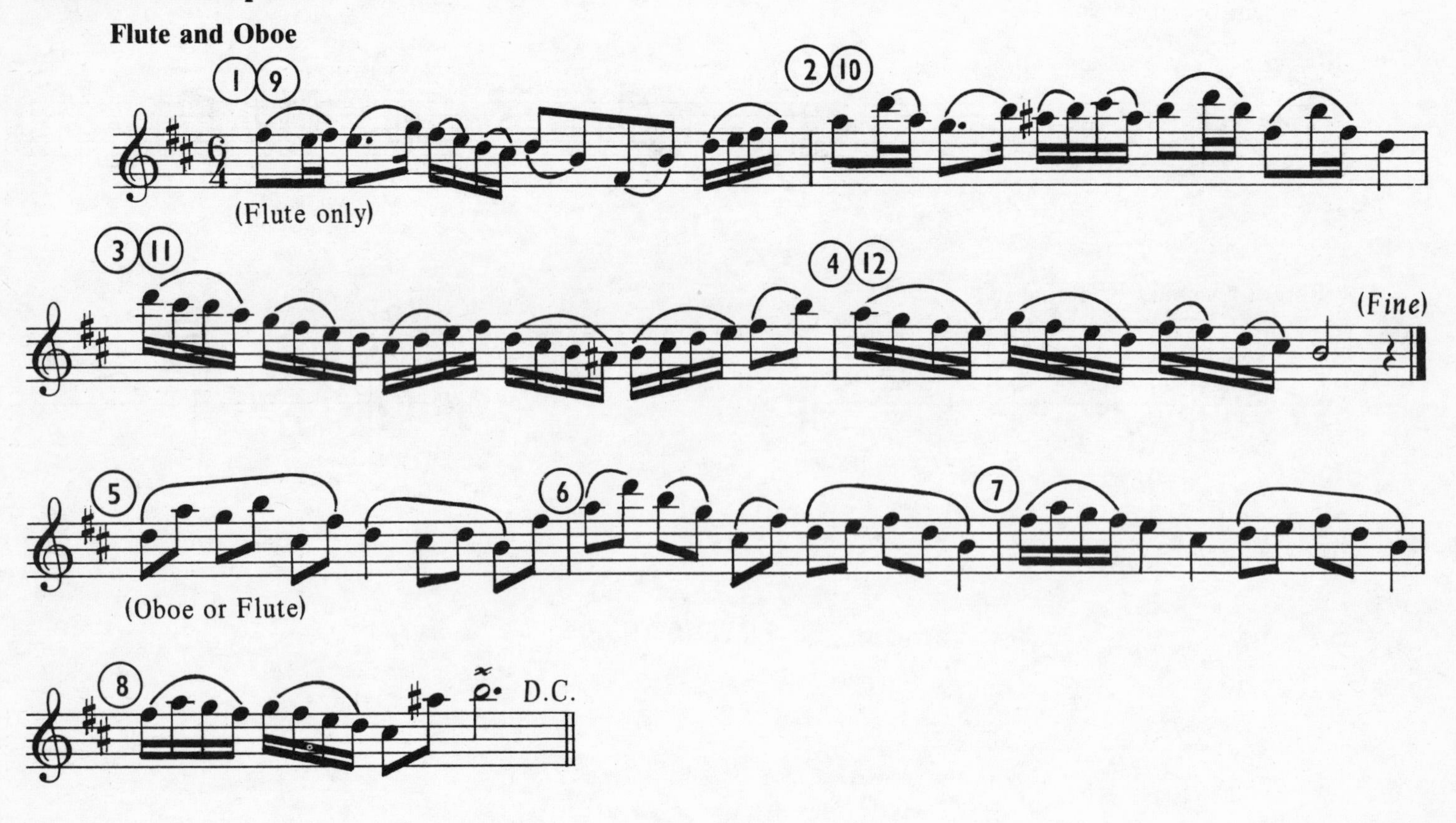

Instrumental Trio

Instrumental Quartet

ALLELUIA

Basic Accompaniments
♩ = 104
Keyboard or Instruments
Guitar
A♭ E♭ A♭ E♭ A♭ E♭ A♭ E♭
Timpani
Instrumental Solos
Flute
B♭ Trumpet (In alternation with Flute)
B♭ Trumpet
CODA
(Fine)

BENEDICITE DOMINO

Bless the Lord, all you works of the Lord.

Basic Accompaniments

Keyboard

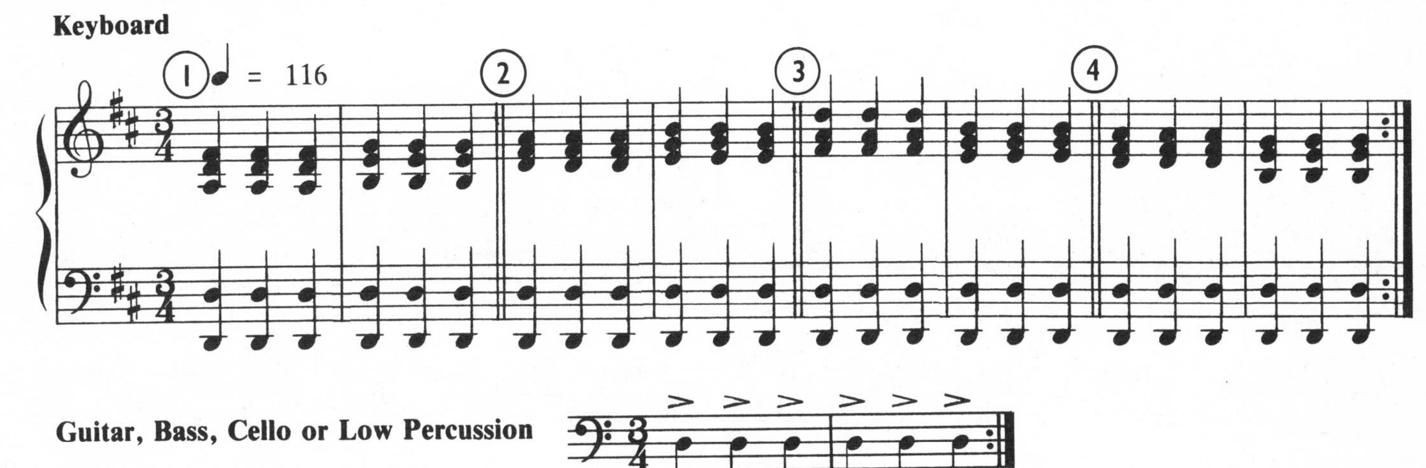

Guitar, Bass, Cello or Low Percussion

Varied Accompaniments and Solos

Flute

Violin

B♭ Clarinet

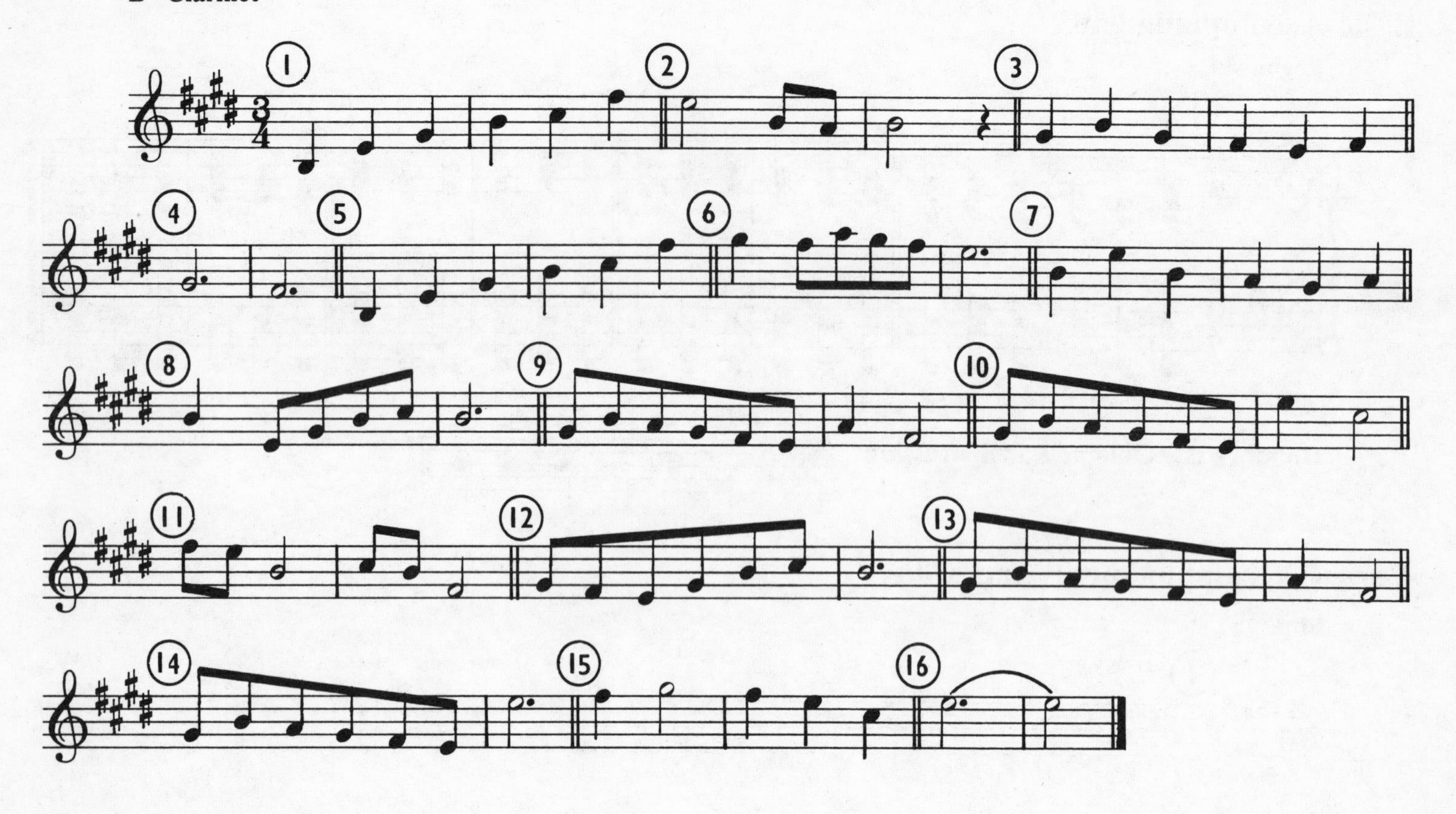

B♭ Trumpet

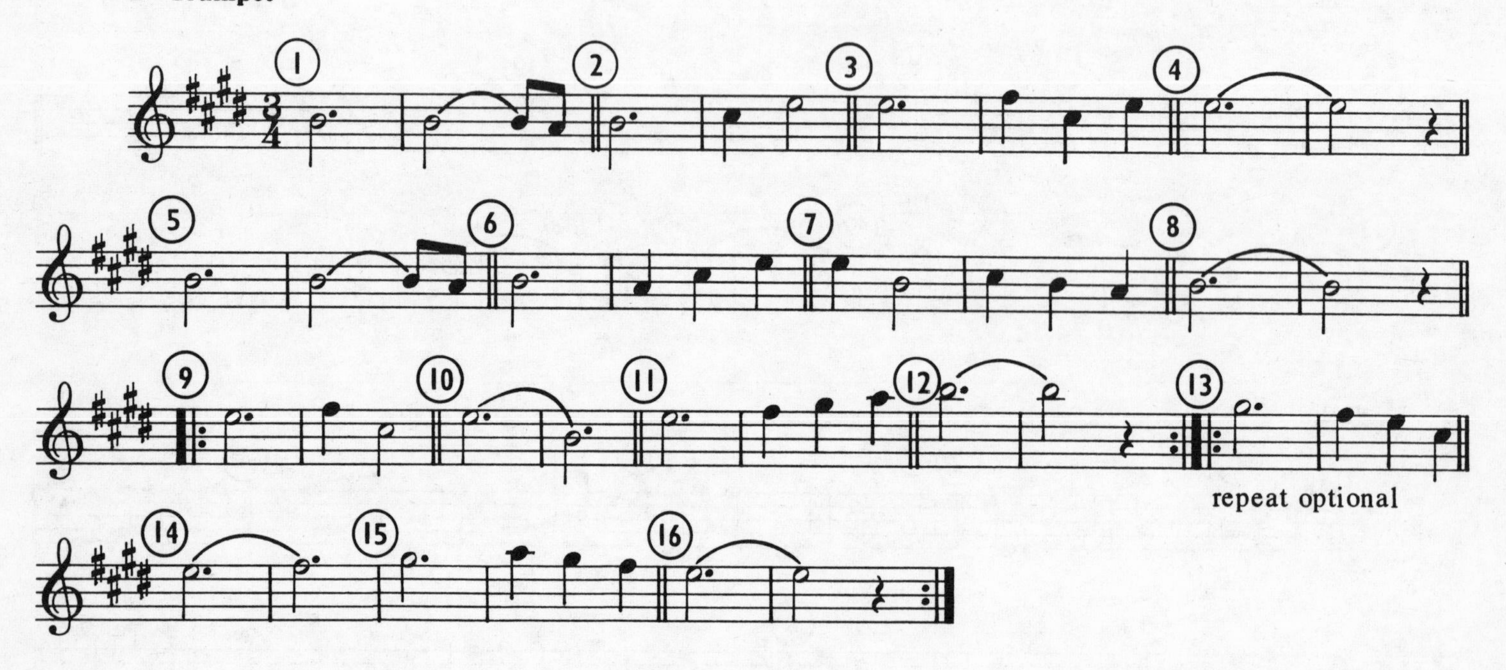

BENEDICTUS

Blessed is he who comes in the name of the Lord.

Basic Accompaniments

Keyboard or Instruments

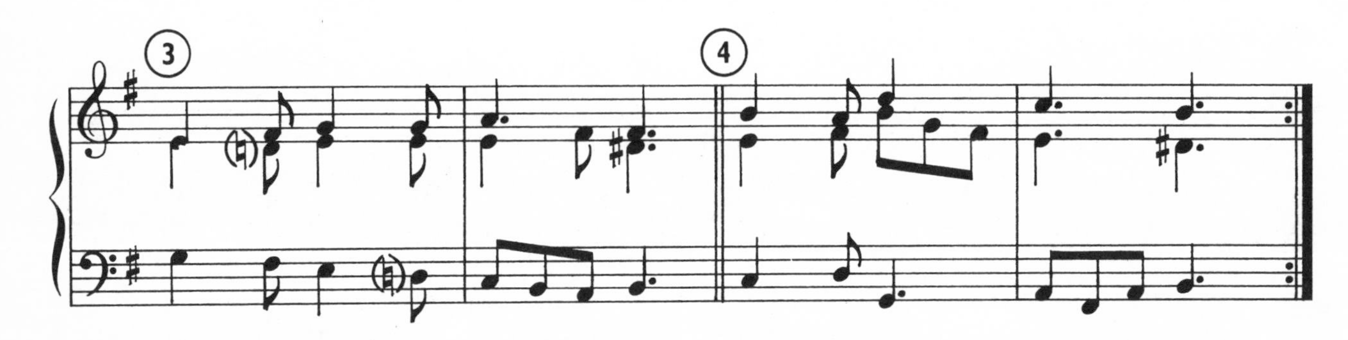

Instruments or Choir

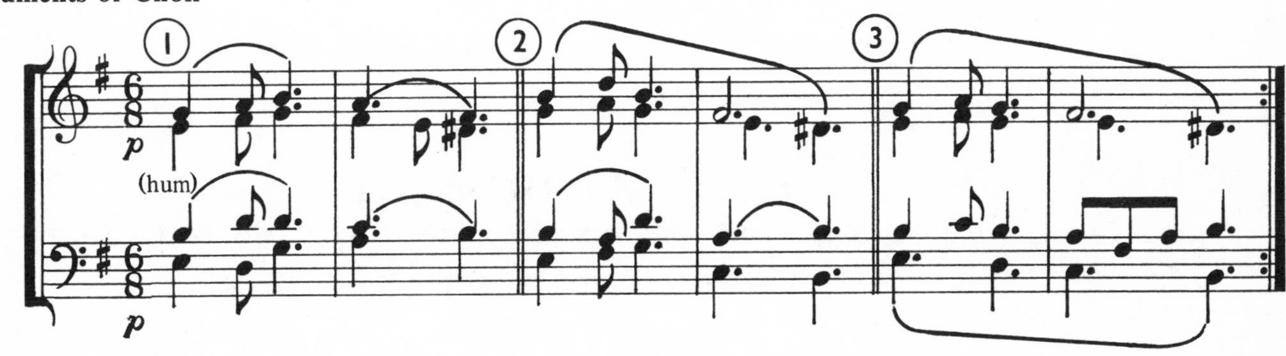

Guitar

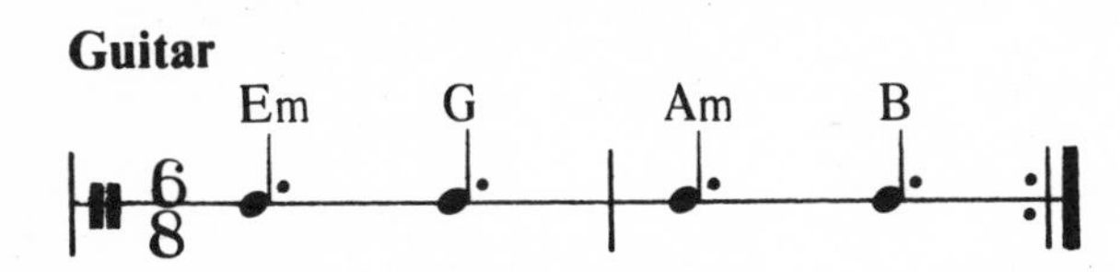

Varied Accompaniments and Solos

Flute or Violin

Oboe

B♭ Trumpet

CANTATE DOMINO

(Four canons and one chorale on the same harmonic pattern using the same accompaniments)

Sing to the Lord, rejoice in God.

Glory to the Father almighty.

Glory to God in the highest, and peace to his people on earth.

Come, Holy Spirit.

The Lord is truly risen, alleluia.

Basic Accompaniments

Keyboard

One can also improvise with the right hand, on the basis of these 2 measures.

Guitar

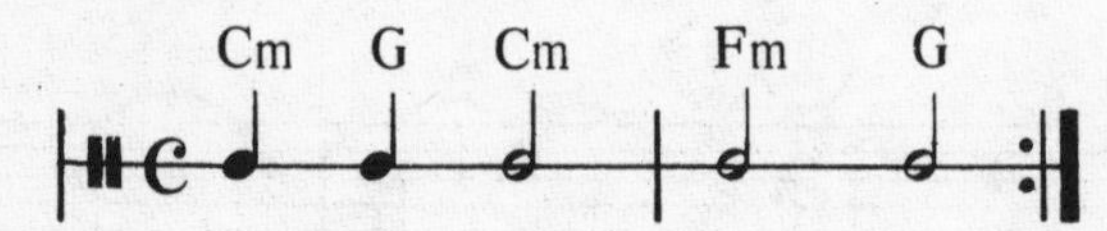

Varied Accompaniments and Solos

Keyboard or Instruments

Guitar

Arpeggiated

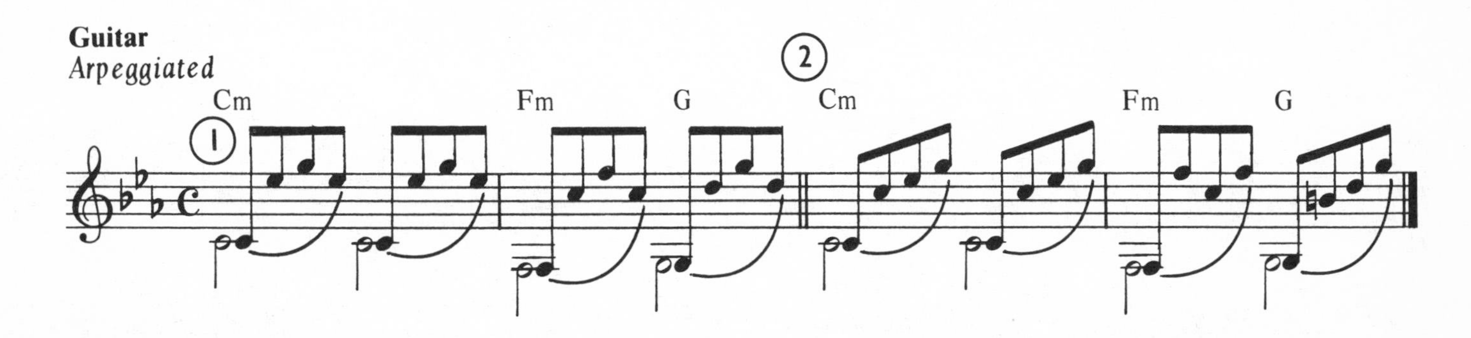

Recorder

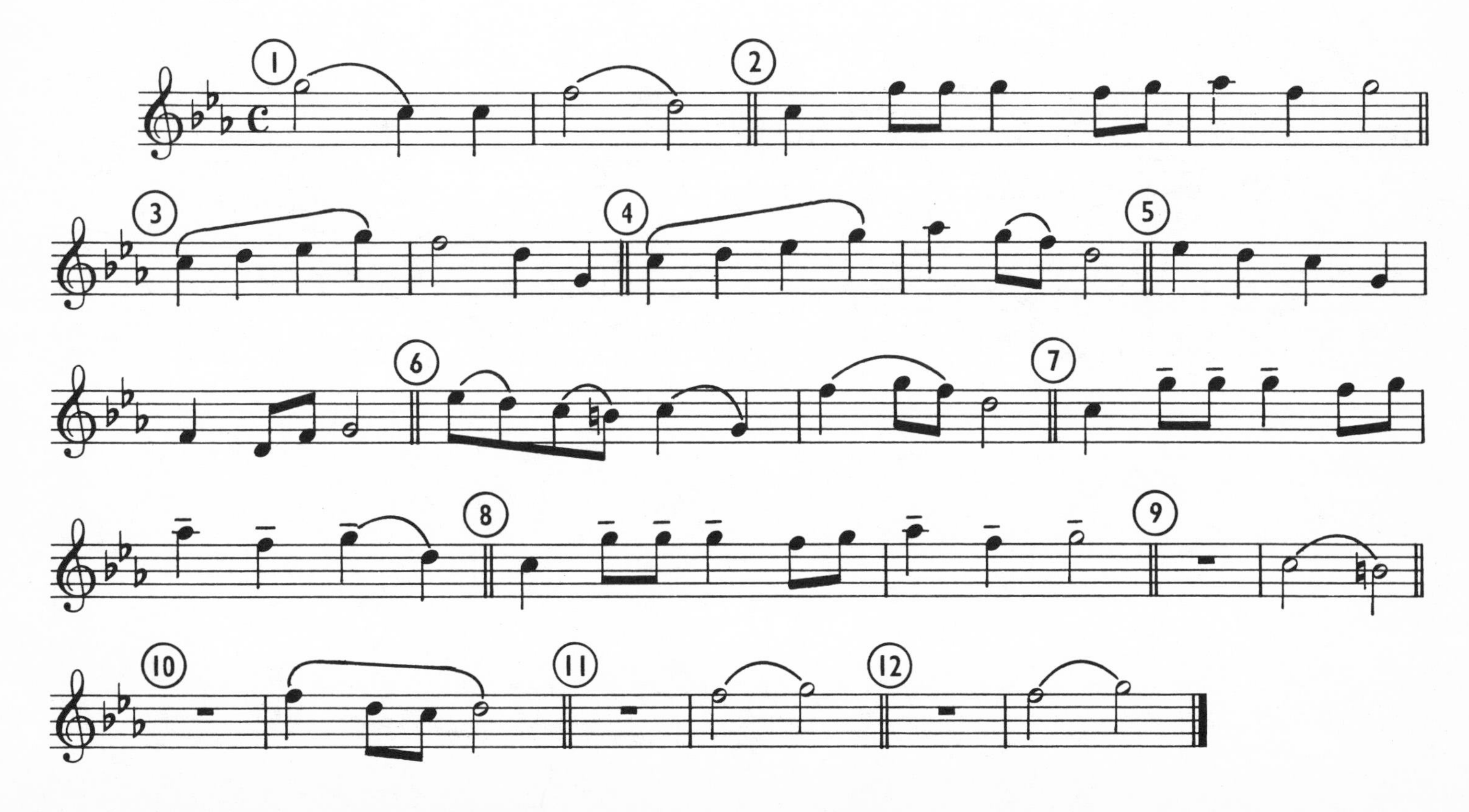

Violin and Flute (or 2 Violins or 2 Flutes)
Each part may be performed separately.

11
12
13
14
15
16
17
18
19
3
B♭ Trumpet
1
1
March-like
f
2
3
4
5
7
6
8
9
2
1
Legato
mf
2
3
4
(echo)
p
5
7
f
6
8
9
10
(echo)
p

Trombone

Cello

CHRISTUS VINCIT — JUBILATE COELI

Christ conquers, Christ reigns, Christ rules.
Heaven and earth rejoice for Jesus Christ is truly risen.

Basic Accompaniments

Keyboard

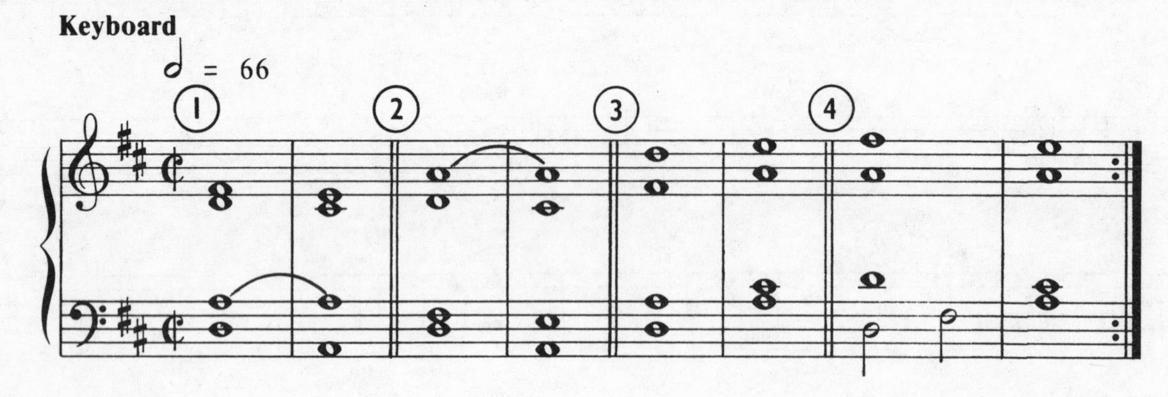

Guitar

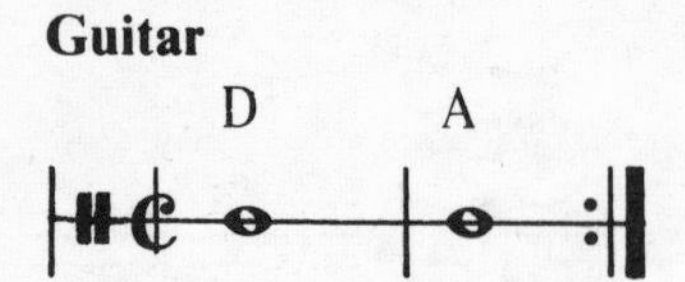

Bass or Cello

Timpani or Tom-Toms

Varied Accompaniments and Solos

Recorders

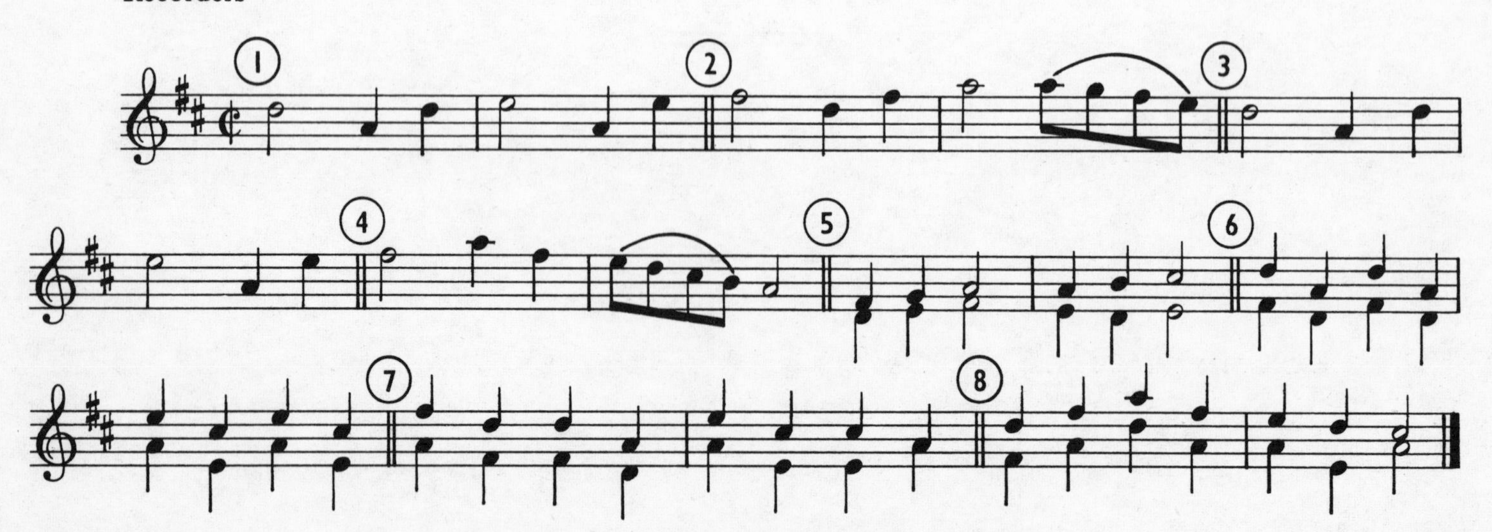

Flute or Violin

B♭ Clarinet

B♭ Saxophone

B♭ Trumpet

Trombone
Solo

Duo with Trumpet

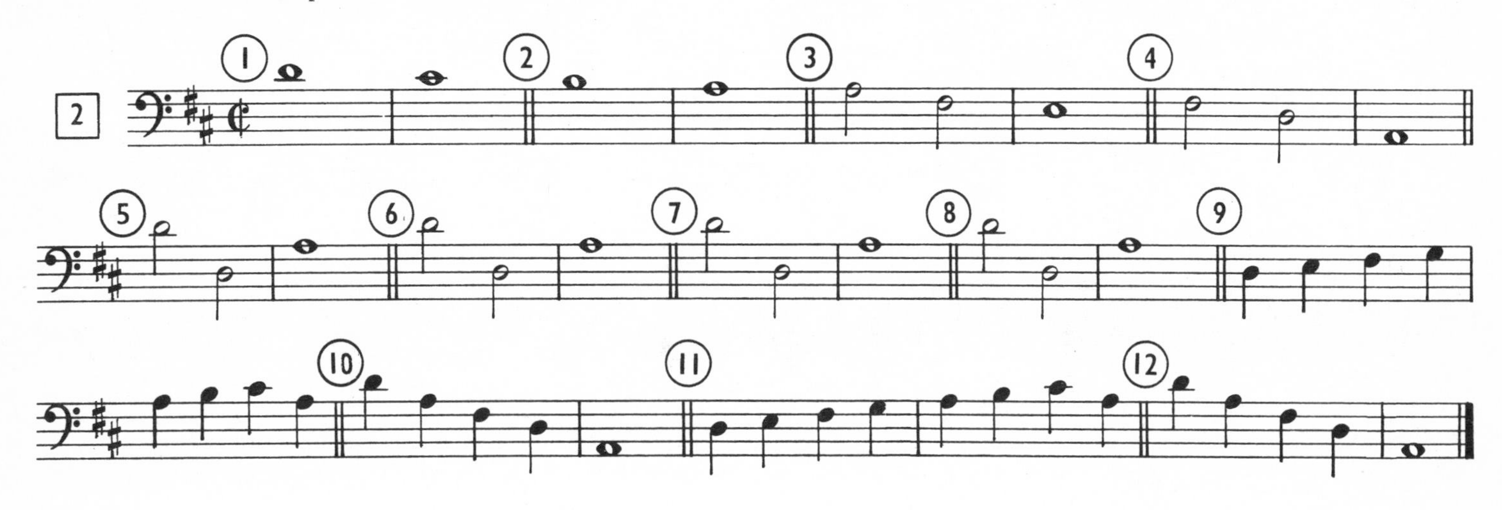

Cello

CREDO II

We believe in one God, one Lord and one Spirit.

Keyboard

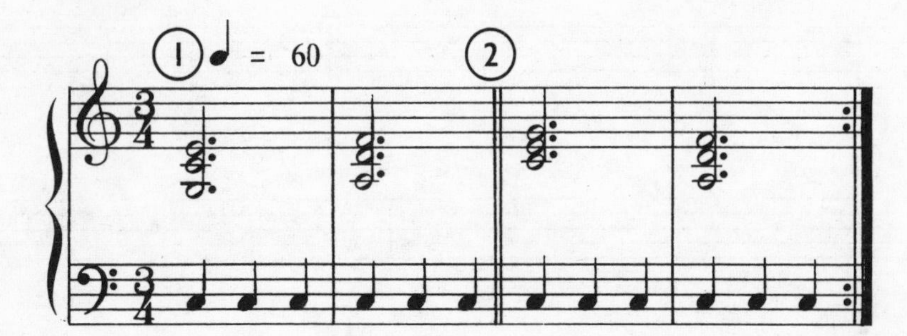

Guitar

Instruments (with bass ostinato on C)

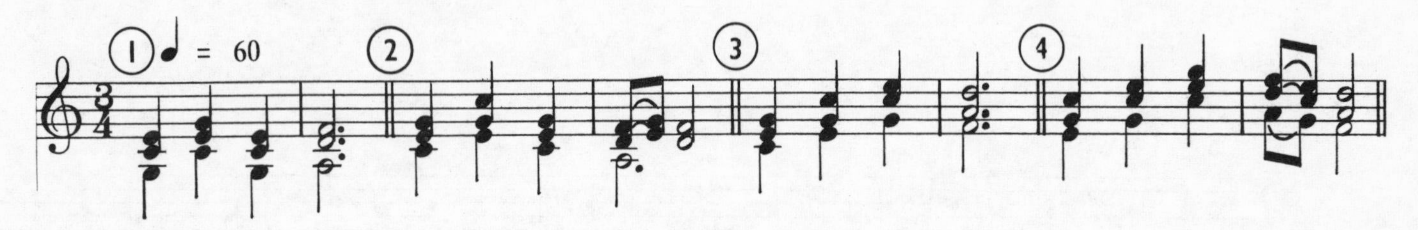

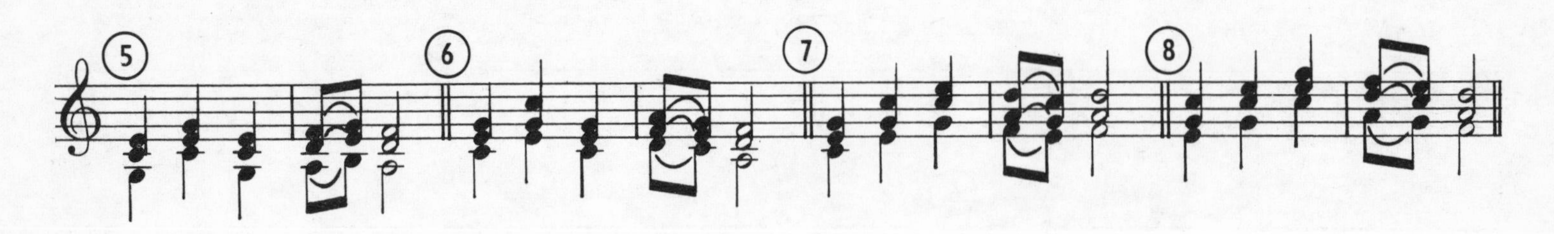

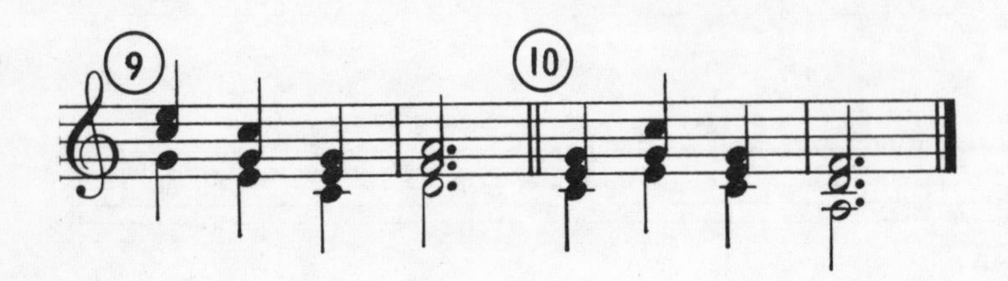

DA PACEM DOMINE

Give peace, O Lord.

Basic Accompaniments

Keyboard or Instruments

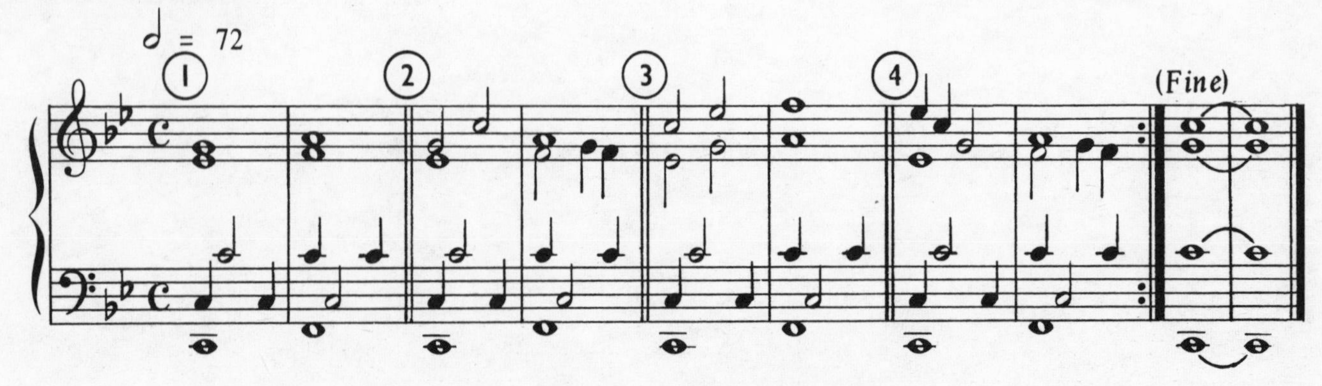

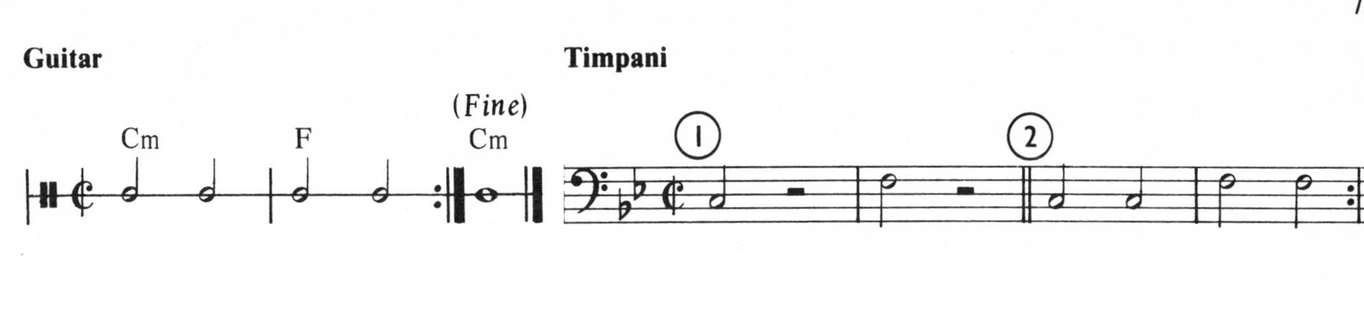

Varied Accompaniments and Solos

Recorders

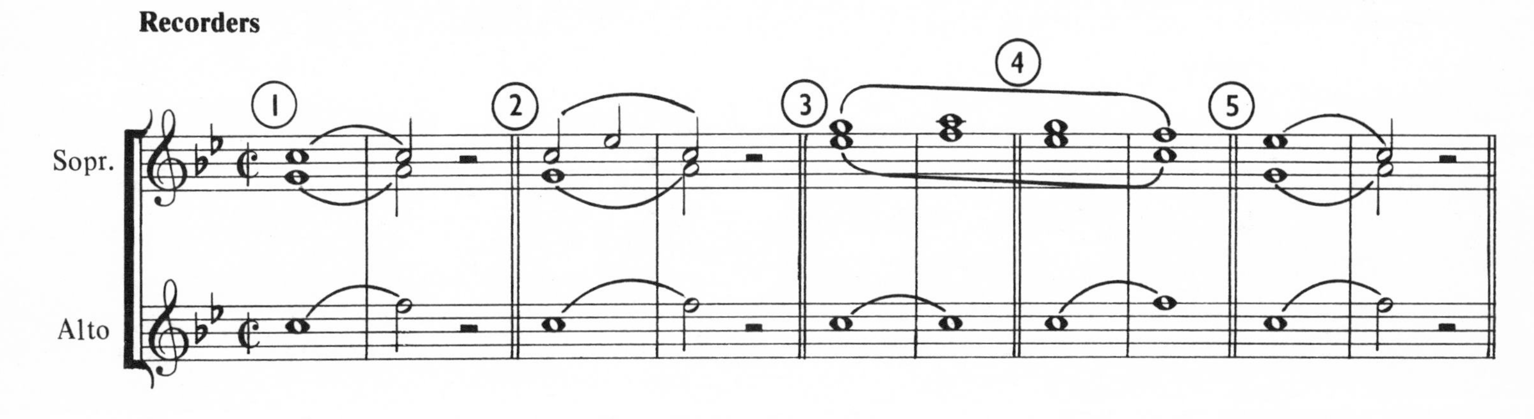

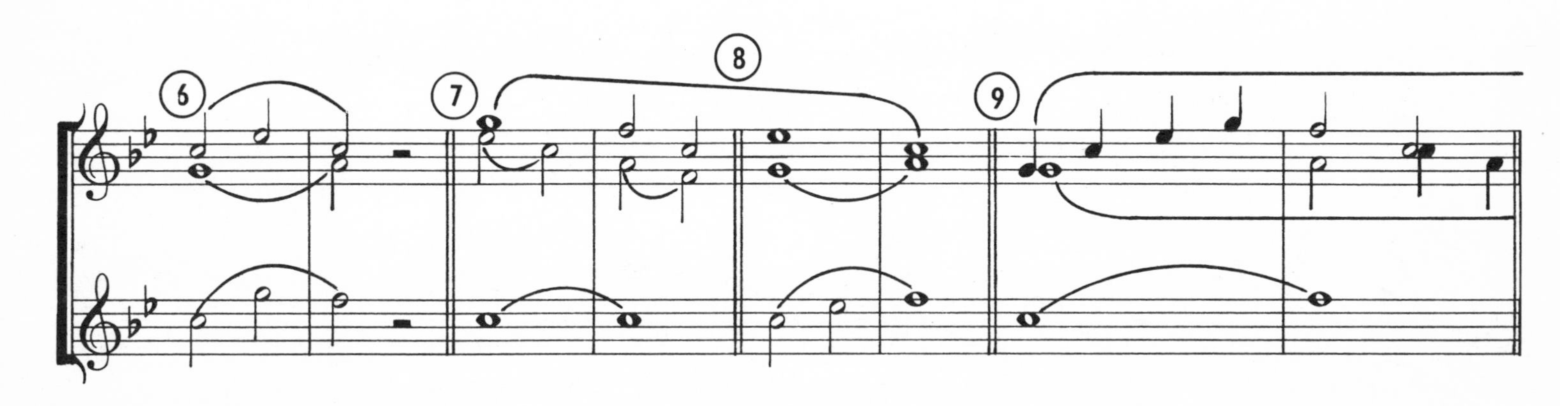

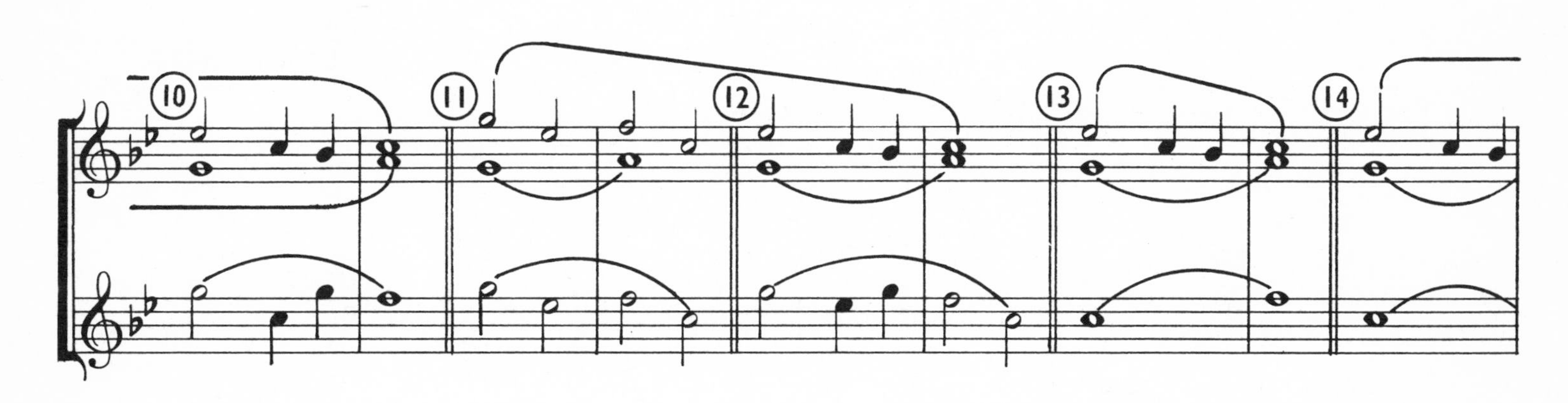

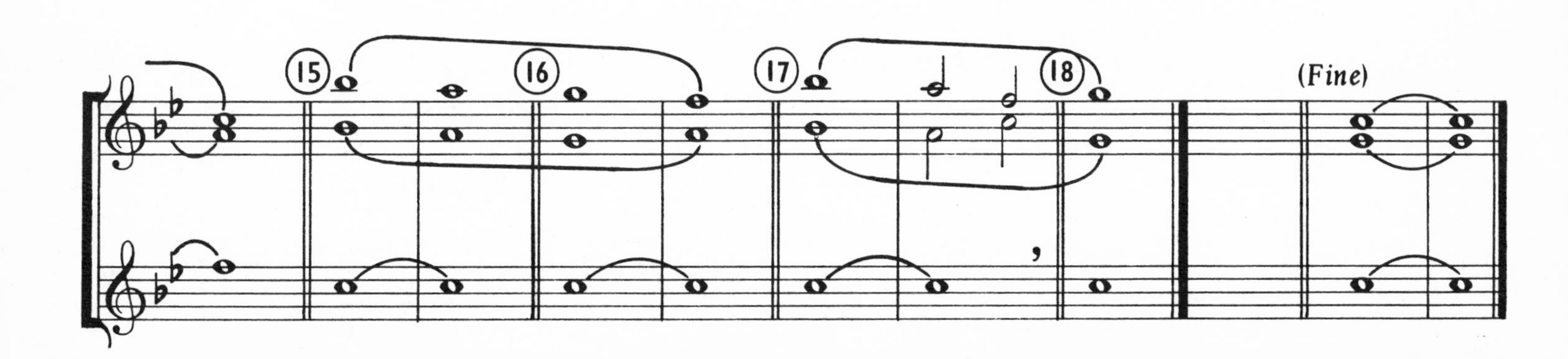

Flute and Oboe Duo
with Choir

Flute or Violin

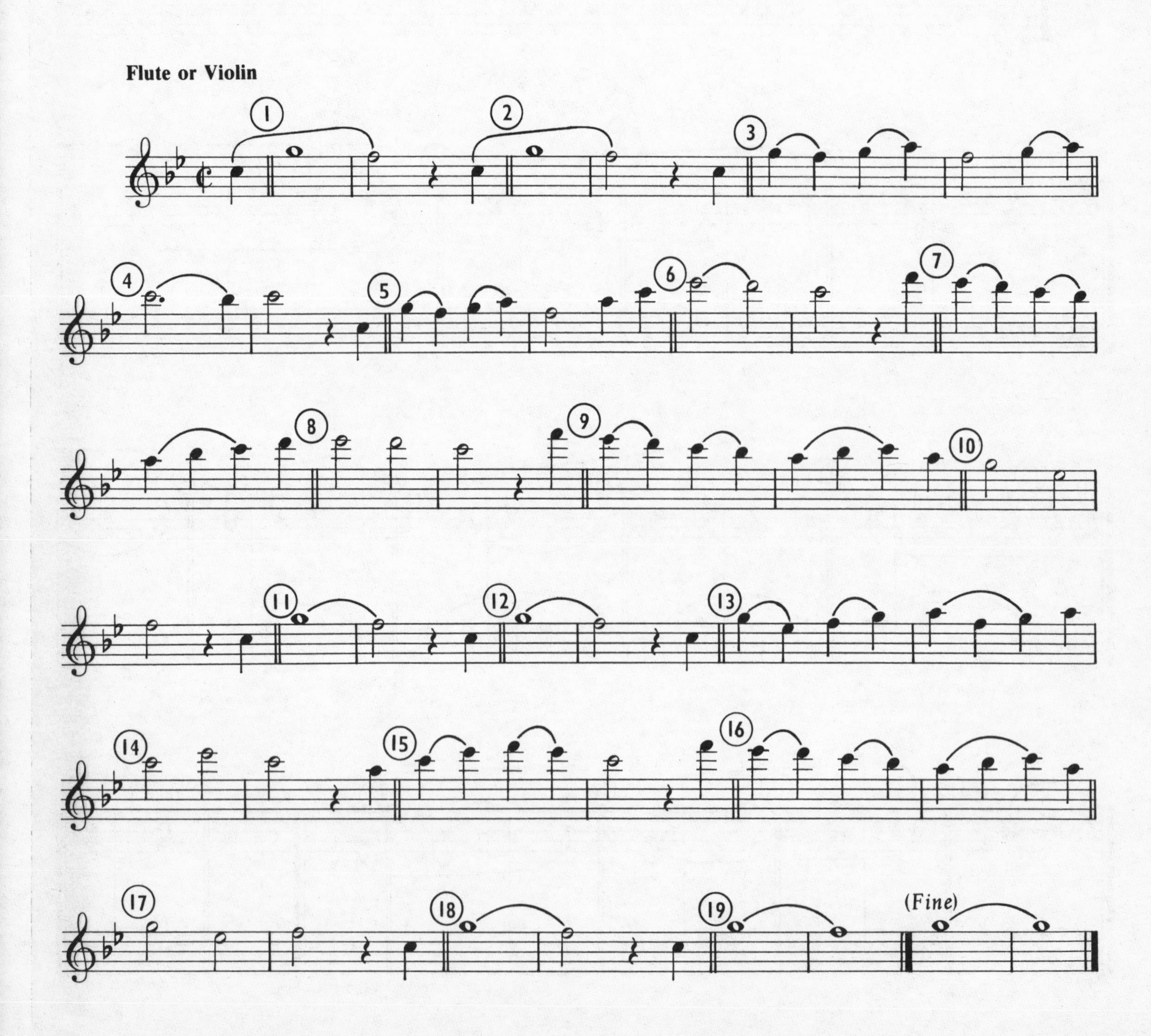

B♭ Trumpet

(Fine)
Cello
(Fine)
Bass
piz.
p
(Fine)

FOR YOURS IS THE KINGDOM

Basic Accompaniments

Keyboard

Guitar

F♯ Bm Em A D F♯ Bm Em A D

Varied Accompaniments and Solos

Flute

B♭ Trumpet

GLORIA III

Glory to God in the highest. Alleluia!
Christ is born today, the Savior has appeared.

Basic Accompaniments

Keyboard or Instruments

Varied Accompaniments and Solos

Flute or Oboe

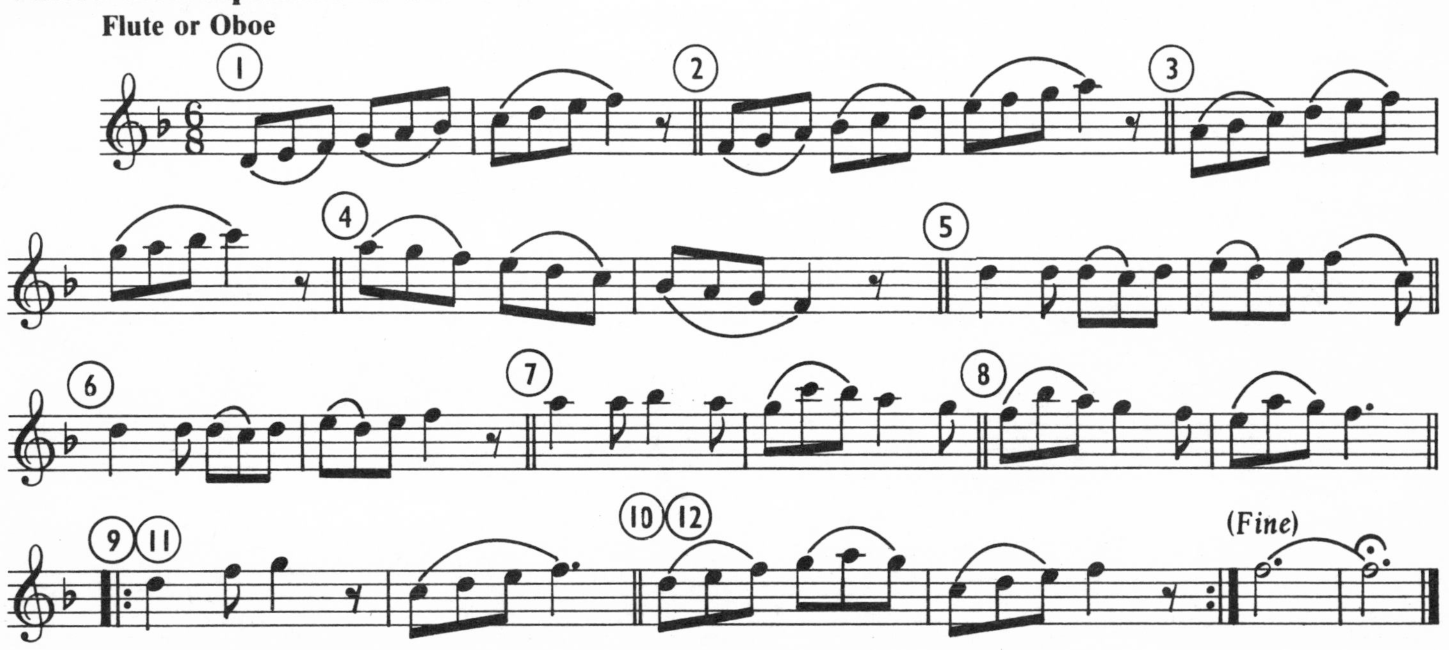

Flute or Violin
(Fine)
B♭ Trumpet
Cello

HOSANNA

Hosanna in the highest.

Basic Accompaniments

Keyboard

Guitar

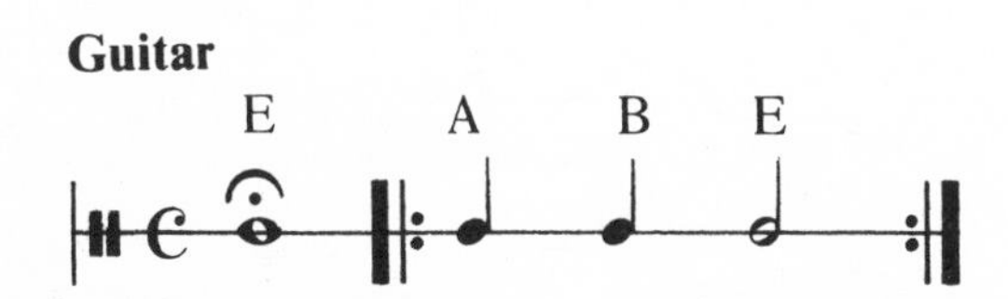

Varied Accompaniments and Solos

Instruments

N.B. For contrast, the instruments may play the keyboard part on some repetitions.

Oboe

JUBILATE DEO

Rejoice in God.

Basic Accompaniments

Keyboard

Guitar

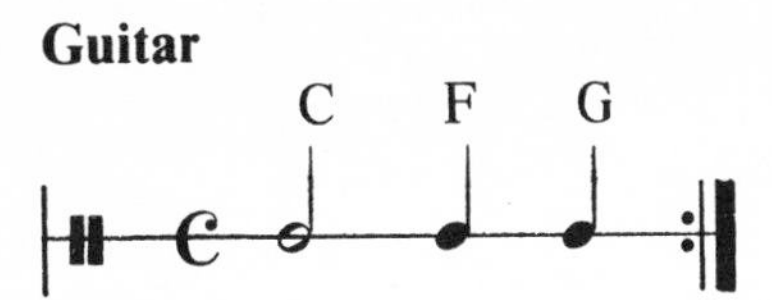

Varied Accompaniments and Solos

JUBILATE, SERVITE

Rejoice in God all the earth. Serve the Lord with gladness.

Basic Accompaniments

Keyboard or Instruments

Guitar

Varied Accompaniments and Solos

B♭ Trumpet

With the last repeat of the canon

Cellos or Bassoons

LAUDAMUS TE

We praise you, Lord.

Basic Accompaniments

Keyboard or Instruments

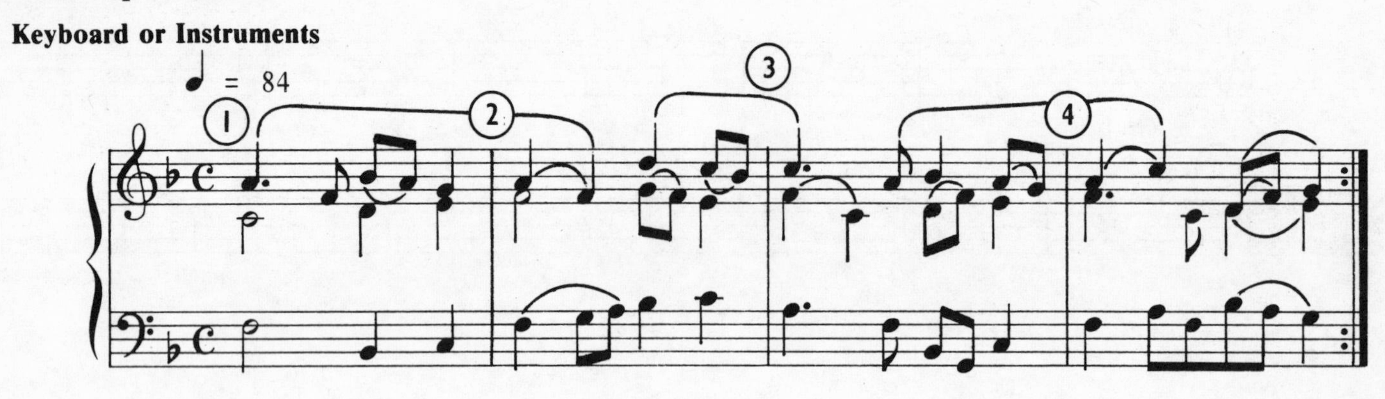

Guitar

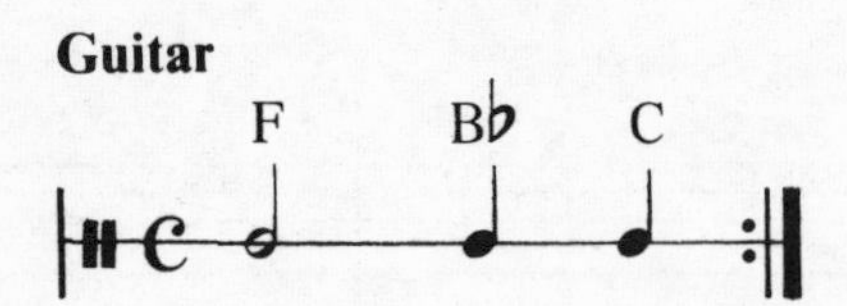

Varied Accompaniments and Solos

Instruments

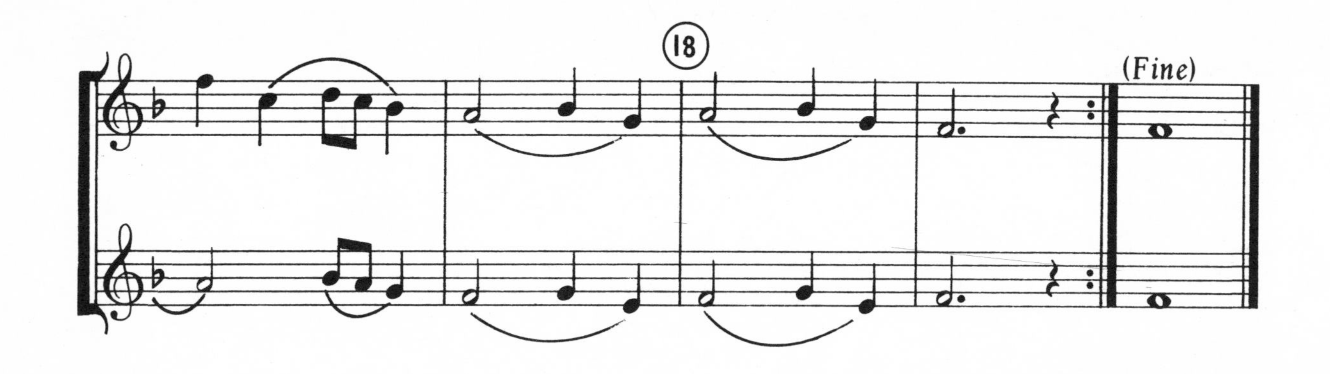

B♭ Trumpet

MAGNIFICAT

My soul magnifies the Lord.

Basic Accompaniments

Keyboard

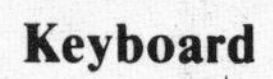

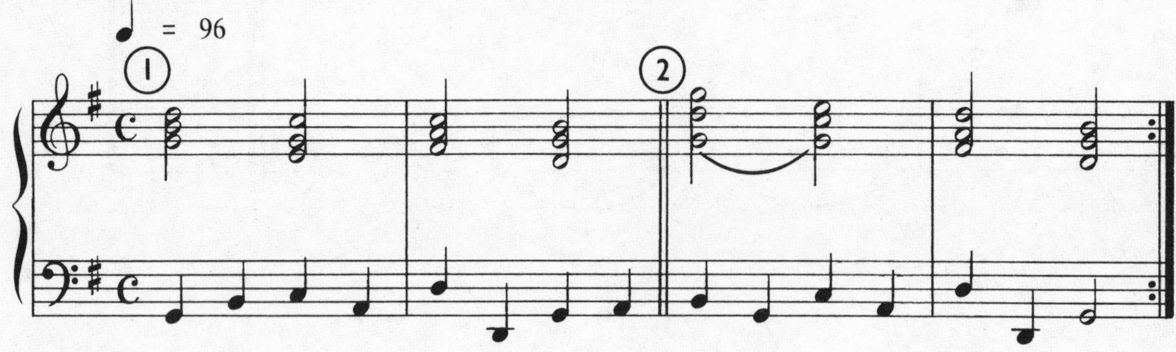

Guitar

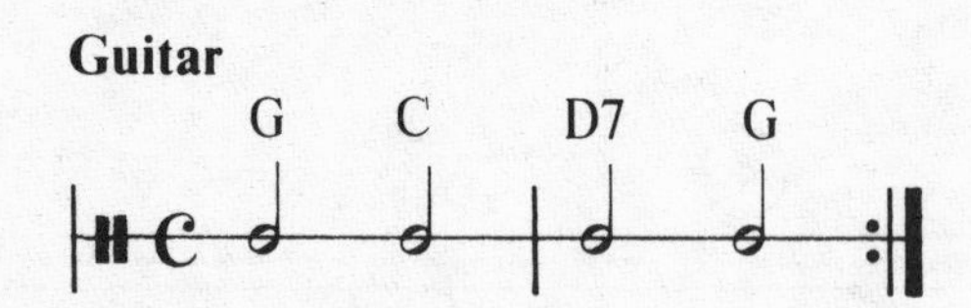

Varied Accompaniments and Solos

Flutes, Violins, etc.

B♭ Trumpet
Secondary Canon Theme
Like a chorale
sim.
repeat optional
repeat optional
March-like
1.
2.

OSTENDE NOBIS

Lord, show us your mercy. Amen! Come soon!

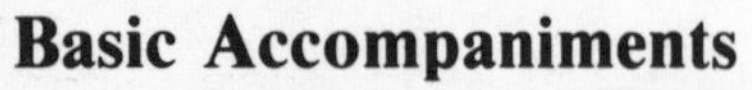

Basic Accompaniments

Guitar

A Dm Gm A A

Varied Accompaniments and Solos

String Trio

Duo for Flute and Cello

N.B. Optional out from * to * (15 - 27)

Oboe

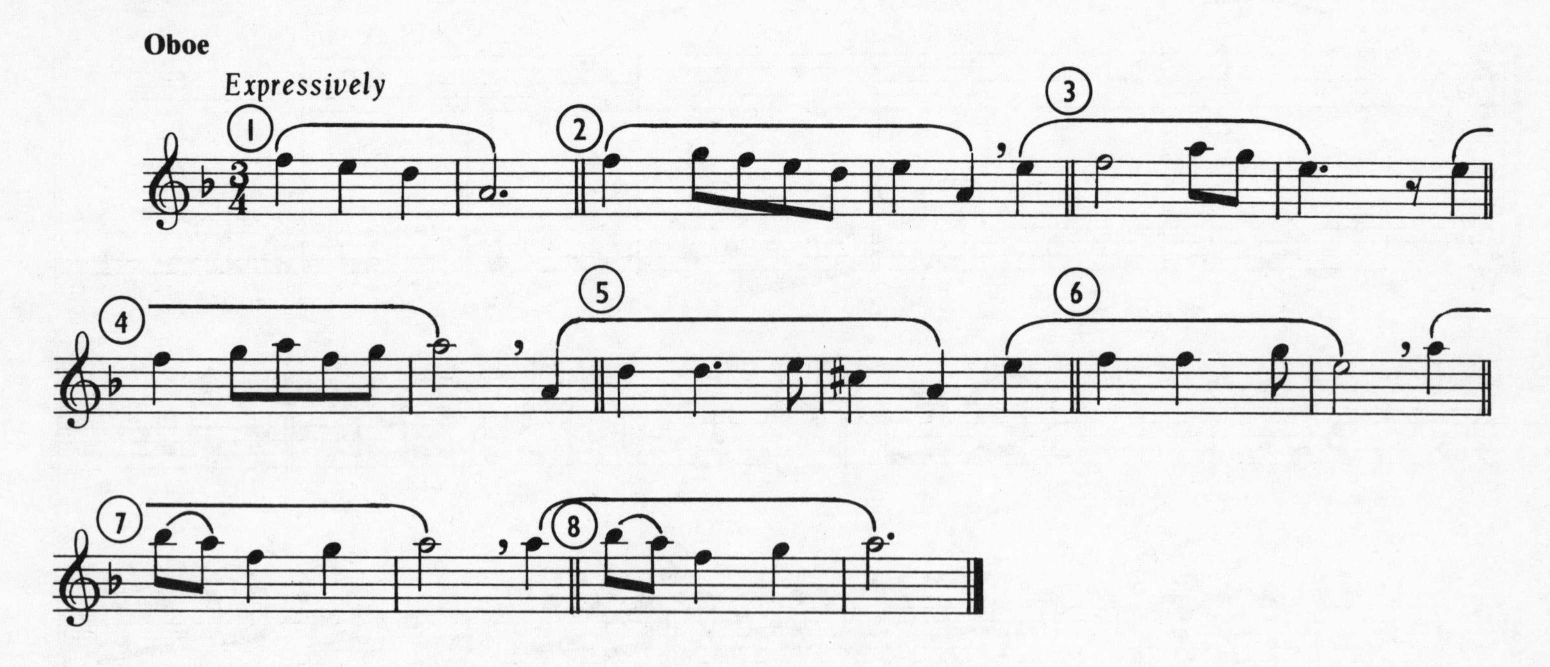

B♭ Trumpet

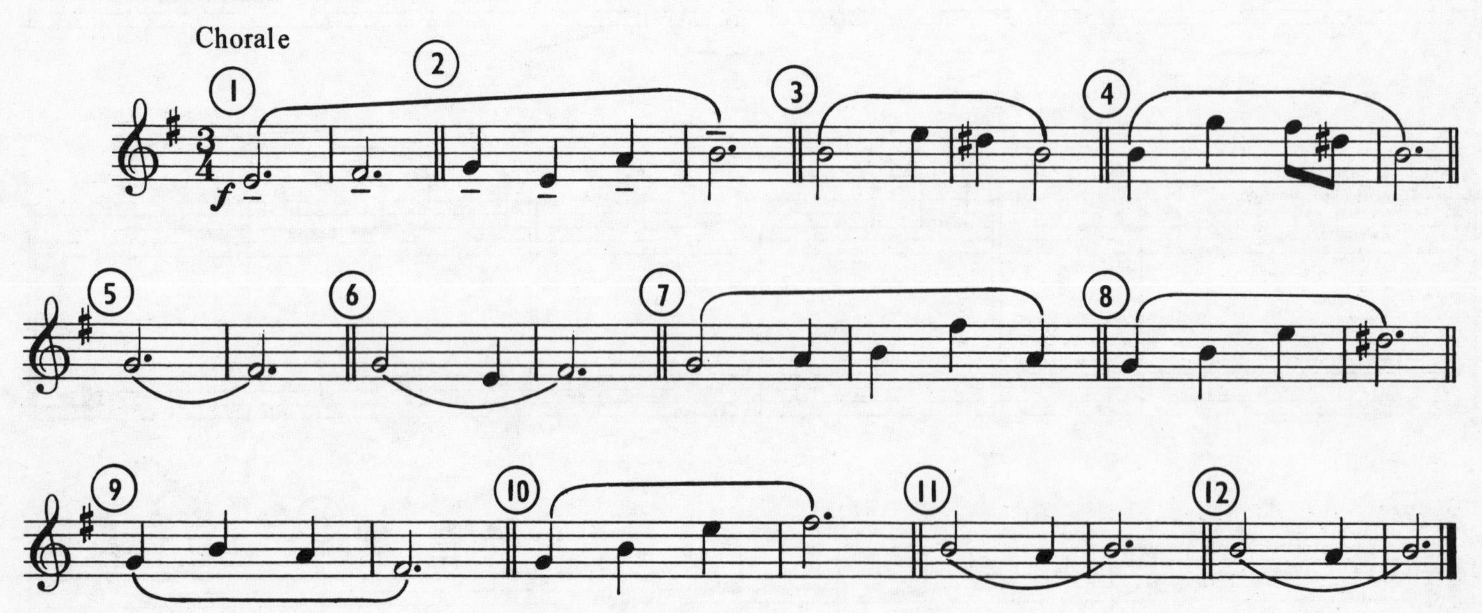

PATER SANCTE

Holy Father, listen to our pleading.

Basic Accompaniments

Keyboard or Instruments

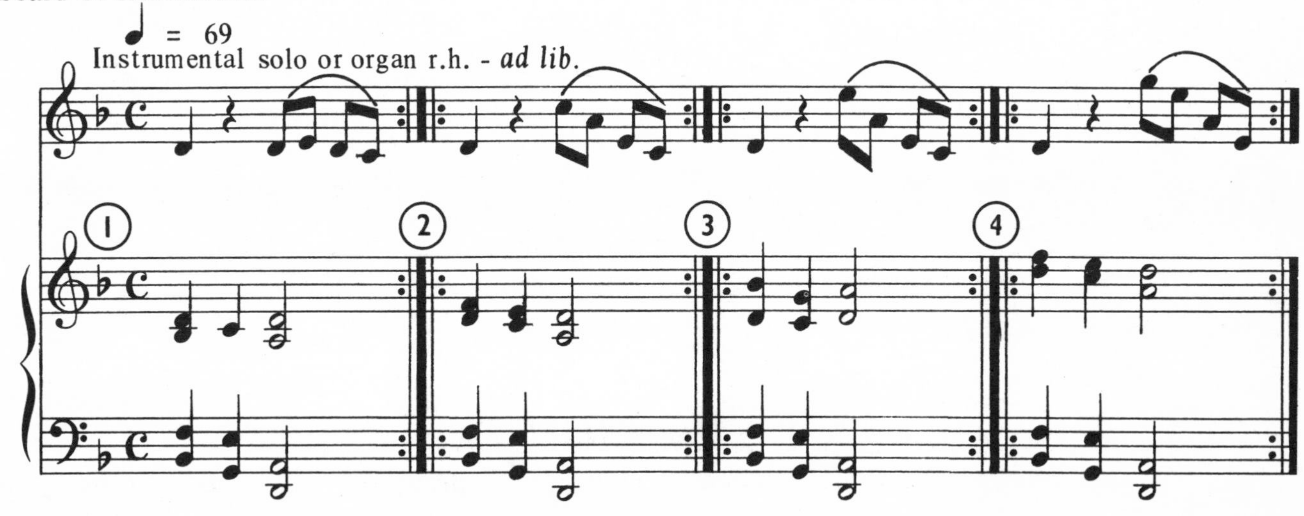

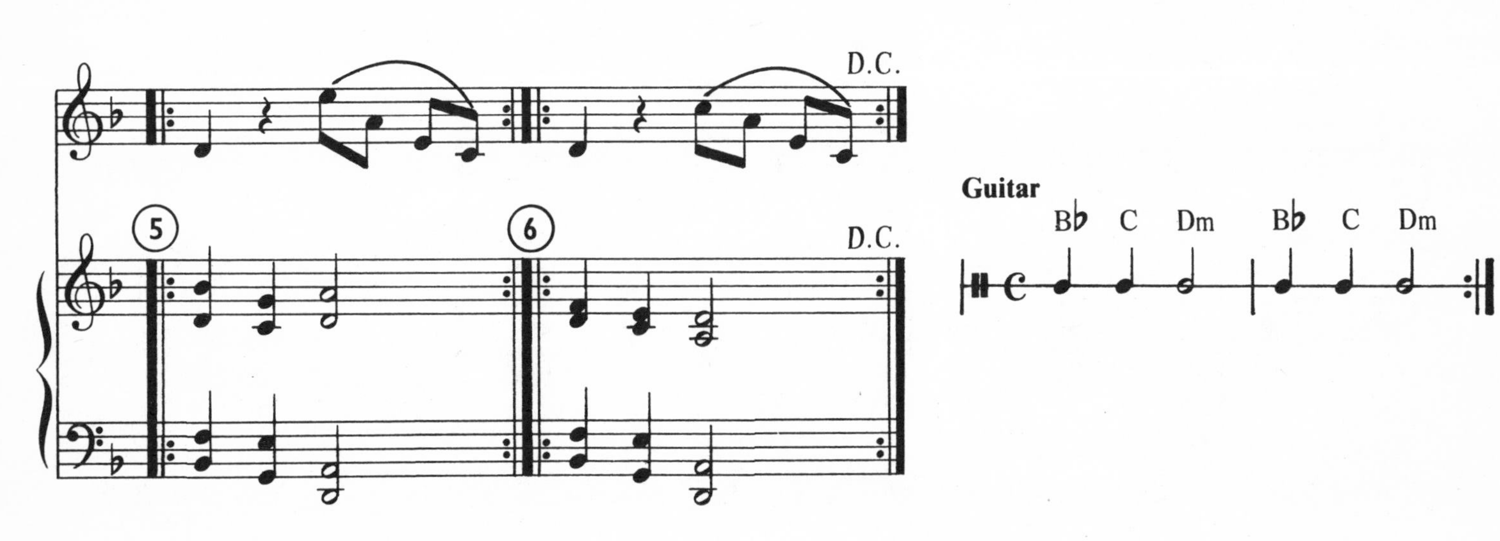

Varied Accompaniments and Solos

Flute or Violin Solo

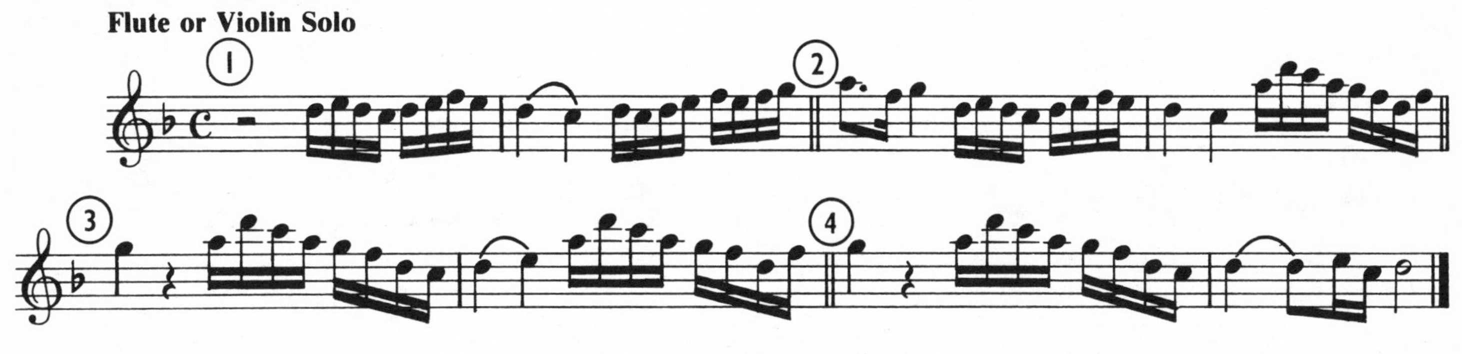

Violin Solo

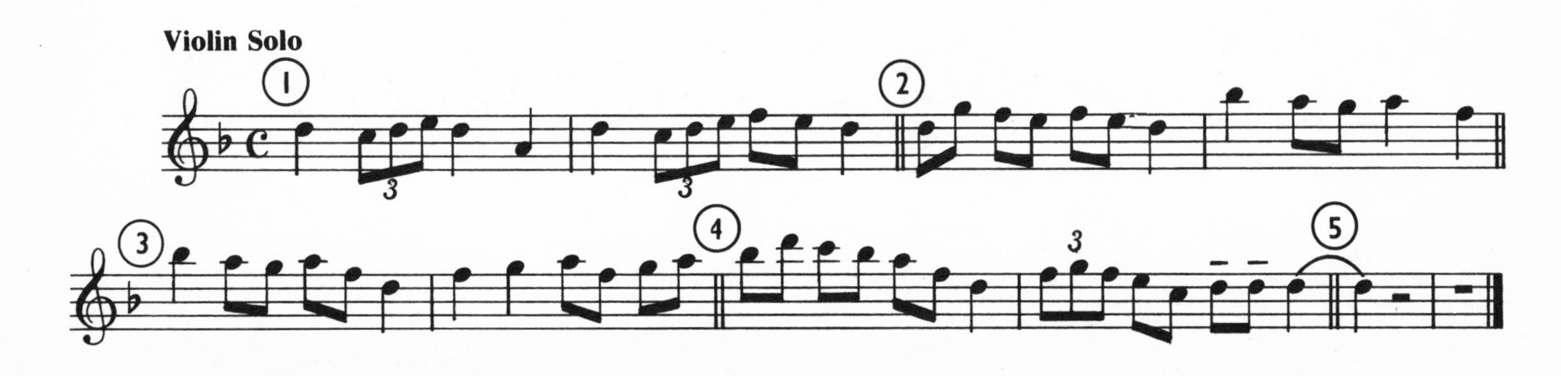

B♭ Trumpet Solo (or Oboe)

PER CRUCEM

By your cross and passion, and by your holy resurrection, deliver us, O Lord.

Basic Accompaniments

Keyboard

Guitar

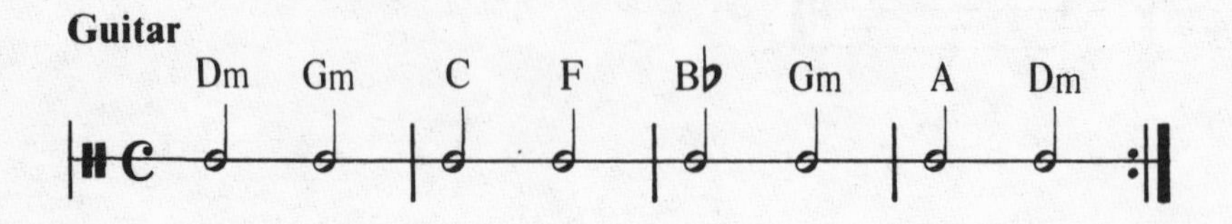

Varied Accompaniments and Solos

Flute

Oboe
1
2
3
4
5
6
1.
2.
B♭ Trumpet
1
Chorale
2
3
4
5
6
1
D.C. optional
Cello
1
2
3
4

SALVATOR MUNDI

Savior of the world, save us, free us.

Basic Accompaniments

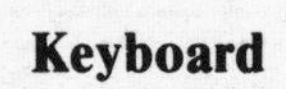

Guitar

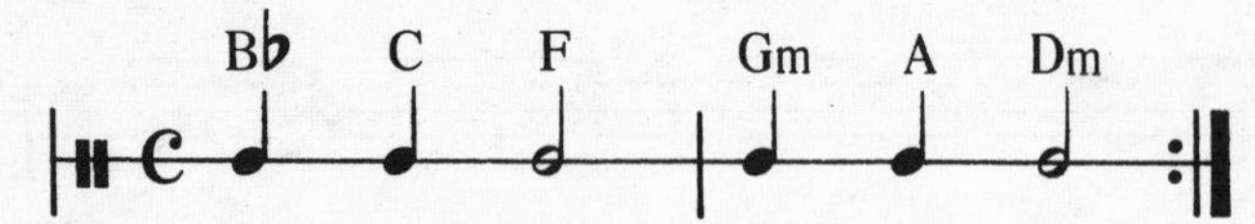

Varied Accompaniments and Solos

Instruments

3
4
1
2
3
3
4
B♭ Trumpet Solo
1
3
2
4
5
6
7
8

SANCTUS

Holy Lord, God of hosts.

Basic Accompaniments

Keyboard

Guitar

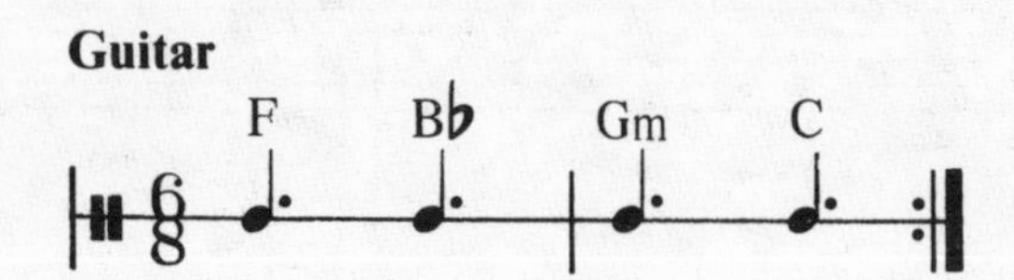

Varied Accompaniments and Solos

Instruments

Flute
1
2
3
4
5
6
B♭ Trumpet
1
2
3
Trombone
4
5
6
7
8
9
10

SURREXIT DOMINUS VERE II

The Lord is truly risen, alleluia; Christ is risen today, alleluia.

Basic Accompaniments

Keyboard ♩ = 126

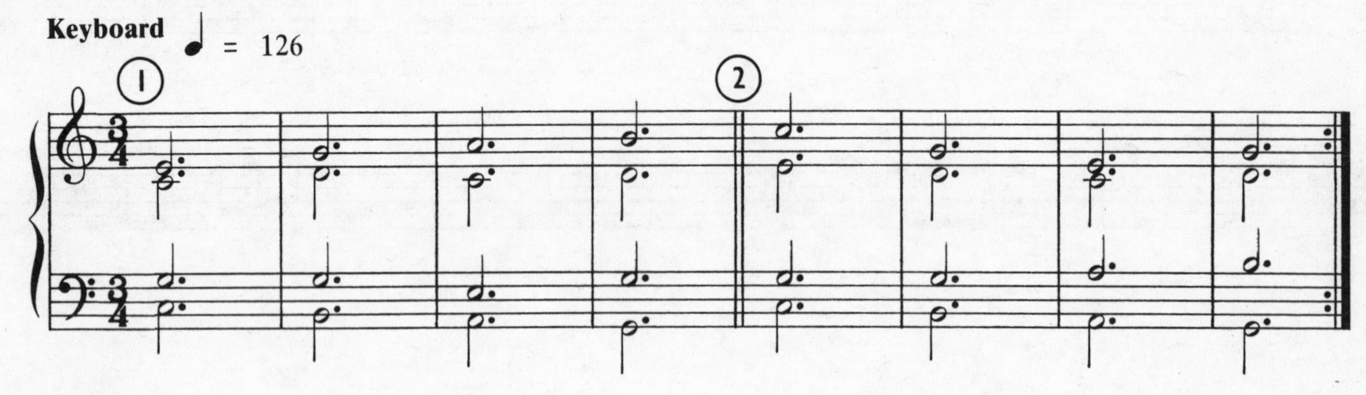

Guitar

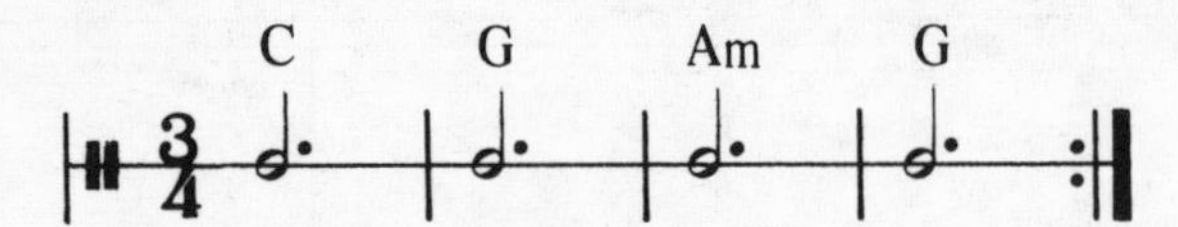

Bass

Varied Accompaniments and Solos

Flutes

B♭ Trumpet
at the end of the canon

Violin

Cello

TIBI DEO

To you, God the Father, through the Son and in the Holy Spirit, be all honor and glory for ever and ever. Amen.

Basic Accompaniments

Keyboard

Guitar

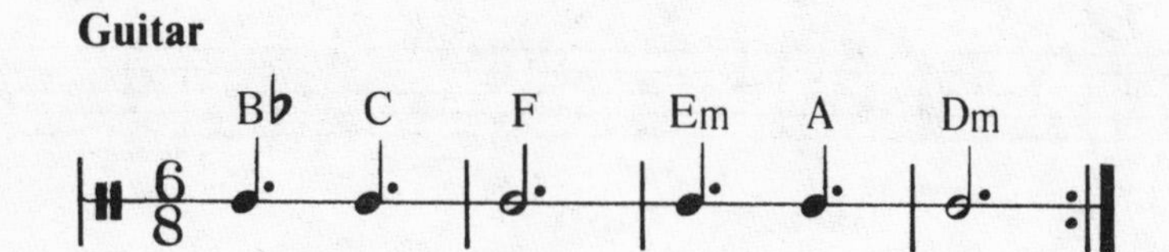

Varied Accompaniments and Solos

Instruments

Flute

B♭ Trumpet Solo

INDEX